92          Biography
ALS                              5341
COLVER, ANNE
Theodosia (Rev. ed.)

| DATE DUE | | | |
|---|---|---|---|
| FEB 7 | JAN 3 | | |
| FEB 2 | JAN 23 | | |
| SEP 26 | | | |
| DEC 11 | | | |
| DEC 13 | | | |
| JAN 29 | | | |
| FEB 25 | | | |
| DEC 14 '83 | | | |
| MAR 14 '84 | | | |
| MAR 18 | | | |
| DEC 1 | | | ALESCO |

5341

# Theodosia

· A N N E   C O L V E R ·

# THEODOSIA

*Daughter of Aaron Burr*

Holt, Rinehart and Winston

New York · Chicago · San Francisco

THIS BOOK IS FOR
JEREMY HARRIS

# Contents

· PART TWO ·

*Charleston, 1801–1812*

# Part One

· NEW YORK, 1783–1801 ·

·CHAPTER 1·

# The Parade

SCOTCH NANNY HAD made up her mind. And Scotch
Nanny had said her say. It was a raw, cold day in No-
vember with a damp wind blowing from the harbor of New
York and rattling the panes of the nursery windows angrily.
No sort of day, Nanny said, to be taking a wee baby outdoors
at all. Parade or no parade, Nanny added grimly, George
Washington or no George Washington, her baby Theodosia
was not leaving the house. And that was that.

Mrs. Burr, small Theodosia's mother, glanced down at
the dark curly head of her sleeping daughter. The baby, as
she lay in her crib between the two women, was peacefully
unconscious of any dispute. But a frown troubled her mother's
gentle face. "Her father will be very disappointed, Nanny,"
Mrs. Burr said. "You know he's given orders to have Theo
go with us. And Colonel Burr is not accustomed to having
his orders disobeyed. He says this is a historic occasion."

Nanny was unmoved. "Colonel Burr may know all about

3

historic occasions," she said. "He may be the cleverest lawyer in New York as some say—but I know my wee bonnie,
and I'll not have her getting her death of pneumonia for all
the generals of the Continental Army or the whole world for
that matter."

Mrs. Burr's frown deepened. She dared not cross Nanny,
for in spite of her fierce moods she was a devoted nurse to
small Theodosia. Yet all the arrangements had been made
to see the great procession when General Washington and
his officers would make their triumphal entry into the newly
freed city of New York. The Burr carriage had been ordered
out and the two older boys, Frederic and John, were already
waiting downstairs. Mrs. Burr made one more attempt. "I
expect you're right about the weather, Nanny, but Colonel
Burr is really quite determined. He feels that even the baby
should have a part in such an important day as this. It's the
beginning of her education, he says——"

"*Education,*" Nanny echoed, and her Scotch voice gave
the word a wicked twang. "It's stuff and nonsense to be talking about education with a mite like this. What's more, education is for boys, not girls." She bent over the crib and
touched the baby's rosy cheek. "Far better for her to grow up
a bonnie lass than have her pretty head addled with notions
of *education.*"

Mrs. Burr turned away, shaking her head gently. She
closed the nursery door just in time to see her husband come
up the stairs.

"Hello," Colonel Burr greeted her. "Is Theo ready?"

Mrs. Burr shook her head. "She's still sleeping, Aaron.
Nanny says positively it would be most unwise to bring her

out at all. Nanny says there's snow in the air. She feels it in her bones."

Mr. Burr's smile did not diminish as he paused to kiss his wife's cheek and moved swiftly past her. "So Nanny says that, does she?" he demanded cheerfully. "Well, we shall see what Nanny says to *me*."

What Nanny said, Mrs. Burr never knew, but before she finished putting on her cloak, there was a light tap on the door of her room.

"Your daughter, ma'am." Mr. Burr entered with a flourish, smiling broadly over baby Theo's head. She lay contentedly against his shoulder, bundled in woolly robe, with only her dark eyes visible, blinking and sleepy.

In the hallway beyond stood Nanny, a starched image of disapproval. But Nanny's opinions, however fierce, were kept to herself this time. Colonel Burr had spoken and Colonel Burr had a way about him that made a body say yes when she meant no. And that, Nanny reflected grimly, was that.

"Never fear, Nanny," Mr. Burr called back as he hurried down the stairs. "Your bonnie shall be on the steps of Trinity Church and hobnob with the most distinguished citizens of New York to watch the conquering hero. And if she should take cold—which I'll warrant she won't—I promise to sit up nights and rub her chest with camphor oil myself!"

So it was that baby Theodosia Burr was one of the cheering crowd that witnessed the triumphant march of General George Washington and his Continental officers along Broadway on that November afternoon in 1783.

It was a day of celebration and thanksgiving for the whole city. Eight long years New York had been held in the grip of war, its people divided, its commerce throttled. Two terrible fires had ravaged homes and businesses, and many buildings lay in ruins. But now the Revolutionary War was ended, and the last of the British redcoat troops had been evacuated. New York, capital of the new nation, was free.

As General Washington and his men passed the steps of old Trinity Church, a great shout went up from the close-pressed crowd. Hats were flung into the air, women waved their handkerchiefs and tossed flowers into the path of the soldiers.

Colonel Burr, standing beside his wife, with little Theo in his arms and the two boys at his side, watched quietly. These were the officers with whom he had served. His record in the army had been a brilliant one. For a while he had been, along with Alexander Hamilton, an aide to General Washington. Later he had been given command of the regiment, and his courage and military skill had made him one of the outstanding young officers in the long, bitter struggle. Until the last months of the war, he had fought shoulder to shoulder with the men who now rode past him. But a severe illness had brought an end to his military career.

Once or twice, as the parade passed, Mrs. Burr wondered whether her husband regretted not being among the officers in this hour of victory. But there was no expression on his handsome features to give a clue to his thoughts. For all the closeness of their devotion, there were moments like this when not even she could guess what lay behind the calm, inscrutable look in her husband's dark eyes.

Back in her nursery, later that afternoon, Theodosia proved herself a young lady of poise by taking her supper and falling asleep quite as amiably as if she had not begun her education by witnessing the historic entry of General Washington into New York. Nary a sniffle did she develop.

And that, as Nanny would have said, was that.

## ·CHAPTER 2·

# Honey Cakes

IT WAS RAINING and it was teatime, and Theodosia stood
between her two older half brothers at the front window
of the tall, narrow house in Maiden Lane. The three children were making a game of guessing which carriage that
came down the cobbled street below would be Papa's. Each
time a rumble of wheels sounded, accompanied by the clop-
clop of horses' feet, they waited, breathless, to see whether
he had really come.

For three long weeks Mr. Burr had been away, trying
a law case in Albany. Now at last he was coming home again
—in time for tea, his letter had said. The table was ready, in
the candlelit study, with tea and milk, bread and butter and
jam. Best of all, Peggy had baked honey cakes as a treat.

A dozen times that day Theodosia had gone down to the
kitchen in the basement. Enveloped in a huge apron to cover
her frock, she had sat on a tall stool and watched Peggy, the
cook, stuff an enormous turkey with a chestnut dressing that
was Papa's special favorite. When Peggy had finished mixing

8

the batter for the honey cakes, Theodosia had been given the wooden spoon and bowl to lick.

"But never tell Nanny I let you," Peggy had warned, and Theodosia had nodded solemnly, wiping a telltale dribble of batter carefully from her chin.

Even now, when Theo was a big girl past her fifth birthday, Nanny had all sorts of tiresome notions about things she mustn't do.

A sound in the room behind them made the children turn to see their mother. "Well, children." Mrs. Burr spoke in her quiet voice, but there was an excitement in her eyes that meant she was waiting as eagerly as they for Papa's arrival. "Let me see how you look."

They lined up, the two boys tall and straight, their cheeks still glowing from an afternoon ride in the rain. Theo was between them, freshly starched and shining, from the tips of her black, square-toed slippers to the top of her smooth curls.

"Very nice." Mama smiled approvingly. The next moment she raised her hand. "Listen—isn't that another carriage?" The children hurried to the window. There, sure enough, came a carriage and horses, splashed with mud as no city carriage would be. It must be—oh, yes, it was!

They reached the hall just as the door was flung wide, admitting a gust of slanting rain with the sharp wind. The door slammed shut and Mr. Burr stood in the hallway, shaking the raindrops from his heavy cloak and holding his arms wide.

"Papa—papa!" Theodosia hurled herself at him with an ardor that threatened to ruin her embroidered pinafore and send her parent flat upon his distinguished nose. "Papa *is* home," she cried, over and over. "Papa *is* home!"

Laughing, Mr. Burr stooped to gather up his little daughter. "Yes, my Theo, Papa is home," he echoed with amusement. Holding her against his shoulder, he managed to embrace his wife and the two boys. Although Frederic and John Prevost were his stepsons, being the children of Mrs. Burr by a former marriage, they were quite as dear to him as though they had been his own. "You all look well," he said approvingly.

"We've kept very well, Aaron," his wife answered. "But we *did* miss you. The boys and I struggled with lessons— and your poor Theo was quite heartbroken in your absence. She absolutely insisted that your place at table must be set each day."

"Do you know what Peggy made for tea, Papa?" Theodosia looked up at her father out of eager dark eyes so like his own. "Honey cakes! Just for you."

When tea was finished, and they had heard the details of Mr. Burr's law case in Albany, which had turned out successfully, the question of lessons was brought up.

"Now then, what about these troublesome studies your mama speaks of?" Mr. Burr asked. "Which of your subjects have tried your souls most particularly? Frederic, you first."

"It's Latin for me, sir. As usual." Frederic groaned in a heartfelt way and thumped his forehead as if to chastise his brains for their shortcomings. "The declensions just *don't* go right."

"And you, John?"

John, the younger, swallowed a last mouthful of honey cake with a hasty gulp. "Arithmetic," he answered thickly. "Mr. Barrows says I have the worst head for figures of any boy in the Western Hemisphere." He spoke with such an air of pride that they all laughed, but a moment later his stepfather shook his head soberly.

"It won't do, you know. If you boys expect to study law in my office, you'll have to come to me well prepared. Law is no profession for numbskulls these days. Most particularly as the firm of Burr & Sons will have the wit and eloquence of my friend Hamilton to contend with."

Young Alexander Hamilton rivaled Aaron Burr as the most promising and successful of New York lawyers.

Mr. Burr spoke lightly, but there was a sternness under his words that made the boys realize he meant what he said. For all his devotion as a father, Aaron Burr was a hard taskmaster. He had never spared himself, nor anyone else either, and even Theodosia had already learned the lesson of his iron discipline.

"And now, Miss"—Theo's father turned to her—"what report can you give of yourself? Have you improved your letters while I was away?"

"Mama says the last page in my copybook is the best yet," she said promptly, "all except the s's. They always twist the wrong way. But I've learned my numbers—and two new French songs from Mama."

"Excellent. I shall hear them tomorrow." Mr. Burr drew his chair nearer to the fire. A quiet peacefulness settled over the room. Only the sound of a baker's boy crying his wares sounded from the street outside. The lonely voice, half drowned by the splashing torrent of rain, made the room seem even cozier. The boys were bent over their books. Mrs. Burr took up her sewing.

Presently Theodosia climbed onto her father's knee. Her bright head rested against his safely encircling arm.

Papa was home once more. All was well.

## CHAPTER 3

# Richmond Hill

W HEN THE HEAT of summer descended on New
York, bringing in its wake the annual scourge of
yellow fever, the Burr family left for the country, where
they stayed in a rambling farmhouse overlooking Long Island Sound at Pelham.

The children could roam through the woods and fields,
and spend long hours on the beach, where the east breezes
blew fresh and cool. They grew brown in the sun, and appe-
tites that had waned languidly in the city became suddenly
ravenous. Mr. Burr, journeying out from town as often as
his busy law practice would allow, vowed he had never seen
three young ones eat so much or grow so fast.

There were fishing trips and horses to ride and drives
along winding country roads. Encouraged by the example
of her sturdy brothers, Theodosia learned to fish and swim
and climb trees in the old orchard, but she loved best the
hours of riding a plump pony, Duchess, borrowed from a
neighboring farm.

The last week before their return to New York was the happiest. Mr. Burr arranged his affairs in town so that he might spend the whole of it in Pelham, and for seven days he was on hand morning, noon, and night. He rode with the boys, led them on walks in the woods, and joined them for picnics on the shore.

In spite of the pleasure of summer, the three children had kept to their studies faithfully. Mr. Burr's system of education allowed for no vacations. Each morning and evening found the boys and Theodosia busily at work, reading, writing, parsing, and translating. Their brown fists clutched pens and pencils; their foreheads knotted industriously, sometimes despairingly, over phrases that would not construe and sums that refused to come right. But always they struggled on until the daily task, ordered by Papa, was done.

Copybooks must be neat and correct to show Mr. Burr, and carelessness was no more to be tolerated in the sunny schoolroom in Pelham than at the house in Maiden Lane.

When the morning of leave-taking came and the carriages, piled high with luggage, stood before the door ready for the journey back to town, the children made a farewell round of the farm. Each horse must be given a parting treat of carrots and sugar before the family climbed into the waiting carriage.

At noon they stopped beside a pleasant meadow to eat lunch. While Peggy unpacked hampers of cold chicken, bread and milk, and fresh-baked cookies, the children begged Papa for a story. Mr. Burr entertained them with their favorite account of how his uncle used to punish him.

Punishments, when Mr. Burr was a boy, had been taken

very seriously. But he maintained that his stern and puritanical uncle, with whom he had lived after the death of his parents, made an even more elaborate ceremony of chastising his nephew than did most parents of the time. Always, said Mr. Burr, there were three stages in the ordeal.

First would come the summons to his uncle's study, and there small Aaron would be lectured on his shortcomings in general and his most recent misbehavior.

Next, in the presence of the assembled family, there would be a prayer for the improvement and salvation of the young sinner.

After which came the third and final stage—the whipping.

"I could always tell," Mr. Burr concluded, "just how bad the whipping was going to be by counting how many minutes Uncle prayed over me."

It was by no means a happy or peaceful boyhood that Mr. Burr recalled, but it was typical of him to gloss over the loneliness and difficulties and tell only the cheerful parts. When he imitated his uncle's long face and pious despair over a wayward nephew, the children howled with laughter.

"All the same," Mr. Burr said, "it was good training Uncle gave me—though I didn't relish it at the time. After an old-fashioned Puritan raising, there's not much in life that can seem half so bad in comparison. Provided, of course," he added, laughing, "the child survives the bringing-up!"

There was plenty of excitement to be found in New York during the winter of 1789. The city enjoyed its brief period as capital of the new nation. With President and Mrs.

Washington in residence, the Congress in session, and hundreds of visitors, the narrow streets of the old city hummed with activity.

Theodosia was enchanted by the new sights. Hanging onto Nanny's arm, she would chatter about this and that as they walked along the water front at Battery Park to see the harbor crowded with vessels, or strolled in the Mall, that fashionable and exclusive section of Broadway near Trinity Church.

Often they saw the President or Mrs. Washington driving past, in their canary-colored coach, drawn by four glossy Virginia bays. Then Theodosia would squeeze Nanny's unresponsive arm with excitement and crane her head to catch a glimpse inside the carriage.

With the busy social life of New York, gossip was the order of the day. At tea parties and over dinner tables, all that winter, people talked about other people. In spite of its new importance, the city was still small enough so that nearly everyone knew everybody else. There were plenty of rivalries, political and social, and more than one ambitious career was neatly pulled to pieces in the fashionable drawing rooms.

A favorite topic of the gossips was Aaron Burr.

Mr. Burr, people said, was a brilliant man—no doubt about that. He had been a gallant and courageous officer and his law practice was still growing. But no man of thirty-three should spend as much money as Mr. Burr did. Some said they knew for a fact that in spite of his considerable income, he was head over heels in debt.

What was more, the gossips noted, Mr. Burr was beginning to dabble in politics. Not safe and sane politics—like Mr. Hamilton, who was a staunch Federalist and Secretary of the Treasury in Washington's Cabinet. Mr. Burr, if you please, was siding with the Antifederalists—which could only mean that his sympathies were with the rabble and not with the "best people," where any right-minded citizen would agree that proper sympathies belonged.

Yet if his debts and his political activities worried his critics, they certainly did not appear to trouble Mr. Burr himself. He went about his practice, and when the subject of his Antifederalist leanings came up, he merely smiled and answered amiably that he had always supposed all men were equal in a democracy, and he failed to see what difference it made whether one belonged to the party of the rich or of the poor.

It was at this point in Mr. Burr's career that a great many people began to disapprove of him. But disapprove as they might, they couldn't help liking him. Especially the ladies. He was so charming, so handsome and tactful—and clever, too. Oh, very clever. Make no mistake about that.

The following year Aaron Burr provided the gossips with a delectable new tidbit buying the elegant estate of Richmond Hill on the sloping bank of the Hudson River. Vice-president Adams and his family had been living there, and before that, during the war, the big house with its one hundred and sixty acres of land had been the headquarters for General Washington and his staff, and later for the British commander, when New York had fallen to the enemy. It was there that Burr and Hamilton had served together as aides to the commander in chief, George Washington.

Richmond Hill was a very handsome place indeed, with tall white columns, and broad green lawns that swept down to a fringe of willow trees along the river's edge. "Mr. Burr must have gone into debt for fair to buy such a house," the gossips assured each other. And as for running it, they agreed it would take a battery of servants and a princely income.

Even Mrs. Burr was troubled. "Debts frighten me, Aaron," she said. "I can't help but worry."

Mr. Burr smiled. "Debts," he said, "are something for the future. The future never worries me—so long as the present is good. Leave it to me, my dear. We'll manage."

The children, oblivious to anything so vague and remote as debts, plunged at once into plans for the new home. The boys promised to work like beavers. They would help with the grounds and stables and plant a garden for their mother. "We'll have our own stables now," Frederic said. "Why can't Theo have a pony of her own?"

"I know the place to get one," John put in. "A white Welsh one, very well trained and gentle. Would you like that, Theo-mio?"

Theodosia clasped her hands and gave a squeal of delight. "May I really have my own pony? May I, Papa? Cross your heart and hope to *die,* Papa?"

A few weeks later the family moved. If Mrs. Burr had any further doubts over the wisdom of her husband's undertaking, she kept them to herself in her wise and gentle way.

Before long, however, an unexpected development was to change the whole course of the Burrs' family life.

## ·CHAPTER 4·

# Lonely Afternoon

F OR THEODOSIA THE change was an unhappy one, for it meant her beloved Papa must be away from home a great deal. At those times not even Snow Baby, her new pony, could console her.

Mr. Burr had been persuaded to leave his law practice for a time, and run for election to the United States Senate on the Antifederalist ticket. And his opponent for the office was General Schuyler, Hamilton's father-in-law.

Schuyler and Hamilton represented the thoroughly entrenched and conservative Federalist party. It seemed certain that Schuyler would win. After all, people said, Burr had no political experience, and no real party to back him—only the scattered, ragged ranks of the newly formed Antifederalists.

It was an exciting campaign and a bitter one. Only Mr. Burr seemed to keep his temper. He campaigned good-naturedly, neither slandering his opponents, nor concerning himself about their attacks on him. He was probably as much surprised as anyone to discover, when the election was over, that he had won.

Aaron Burr was the new Senator from New York. He had defeated General Schuyler and the Federalist forces of Alexander Hamilton. It was a victory that Hamilton never forgave him.

The bitter seeds of hate that led to the long feud between Burr and Hamilton were sown in the weeks of that campaign, and though the two men remained outwardly on friendly terms, they were enemies nonetheless from that day on.

And each, in his way, was a dangerous enemy.

Not even the Federalists mourned Mr. Burr's victory more than Theodosia. The capital had been moved from New York to Philadelphia. The two cities were a long journey apart by horse and carriage, and whenever Congress was in session, Mr. Burr, as Senator from New York, was obliged to stay in Philadelphia.

Without Papa's gay presence, Richmond Hill seemed suddenly too big to Theodosia—and much too lonely. Once her daily lessons were finished, there was nothing to do. She would roam from one quiet room to another, read a few pages from a book here, play half a dozen bars on the piano there, and then wander on, wishing desperately that something exciting would happen.

But nothing did.

On one particularly dismal winter's day, Theodosia sat at the desk in her room feeling miserable.

The whole house seemed heavy with silence. Mama was

resting and mustn't be disturbed, for she was feeling poorly. Frederic had gone to Philadelphia to be with Mr. Burr during the winter session of the Congress, and John was in the city for a fencing lesson. Ordinarily Theodosia would have accompanied John, but she had just recovered from the mumps. Now she had a wretched toothache to increase her misery and Mama had said she must not risk the long drive into town. So John had departed for the fencing lesson alone, leaving his sister to be poulticed by Peggy and to amuse herself as best she could. .

Theodosia sighed. She had read until her eyes ached, then she had written a letter to Frederic. Her tooth felt better, but it was too snowy to venture out for a ride on her pony. There was nothing, simply nothing left to do. Idly, she nibbled at the tip of her pen and glanced over the letter that still lay open on the desk before her.

> Dear Brother:
> I hope the mumps have left you. Mine left me a week ago.
> Papa has been here and is gone again. . . . The day before Papa went, we had your good pig for diner.
> Mr. Luet, an English music master, had an elegant forte-piano which Papa bought for me. It cost 33 Guineas, and it is just come home.
> I am tired of affectionate, not of being it but of writing it, so I will leave it out; I am your sister,
> Theodosia Burr

Theodosia folded the letter and heated a stick of red sealing wax over the candle flame. She wasn't altogether sure of her spelling in a few places, but Frederic wouldn't mind, not being nearly so critical as Papa in such matters. Stamping the seal firmly, she put the letter aside and got up to walk restlessly about the room.

It was hateful having the boys away, as well as Papa, and she worried about Mama being ill so often. Mr. Burr had talked of moving the whole family to Philadelphia for the winter but Mama's health had grown worse, and it was decided that she had best stay at Richmond Hill. It would be weeks now before Papa could come back for another visit. On the day he was expected, Theodosia must have her copybooks corrected and ready for his inspection. Her music would be well practiced and her best new frock ready to put on. If it were a good day, Theodosia would be allowed to ride down the Greenwich Road to meet his carriage. Snow Baby would be groomed until his white flanks gleamed, and there would be a blue satin bow on his forelock to grace the occasion. Theodosia could almost hear herself heralding the approach of his carriage with the joyful phrase she remembered from earliest babyhood: "Papa *is* home! Papa *is* home!"

But Papa *wasn't* home now. Theodosia turned impatiently toward the hall and started down the long passage that led to the servants' quarters. Maybe there, at least, she would find company.

Sure enough, a door was open at the end of the corridor. That was Lottie's room. Lottie was a young girl who had been in the Burr household only a short time, and at the sound of Theodosia's step she stood up quickly and greeted her young mistress with a curtsy.

"May I come in a minute, Lottie?" Theodosia asked. She crossed to the bed where the girl had been sitting and looked at a book that lay open on the neat white coverlet. "Were you reading this?"

Lottie shook her head. "Not rightly, Miss Theo. I was trying to make out words from the pictures, but I couldn't make the sense out. I never rightly learned to read."

There was a mournful note in the girl's voice that made Theodosia look up quickly. So, she thought, Lottie must have been feeling lonely and miserable, too. Theodosia perched herself at the edge of the bed. "Sit down, Lottie." She patted the place beside her invitingly. "Maybe I can help you a little. I do pretty well at reading now, except for the long words."

Lottie's gentle eyes shone. "I'd muchly like to learn, Miss Theo," she said softly. "If I could just write a little, maybe I could send a letter to my mother someday."

"Let's begin then." Theodosia settled the book between them firmly and drew a long breath. It was no easy undertaking for a nine-year-old, but she plunged earnestly into the task. Soon the two heads were bent together, and Lottie's shyness vanished as they struggled along, laughing over their mistakes.

"We'll do more tomorrow, Lottie," Theodosia promised. "You learn so quickly, it will be no time at all until you can write to your mother." She paused a moment, held by the wistfulness in Lottie's velvety glance. "Maybe," she offered, "you'd like me to write a letter for you now. You could tell me what you'd like to say."

"Oh, Miss Theo"—Lottie clasped her fingers eagerly— "if only you would. Just to let Mammy know I keep healthy and what good, kindly folks I'm with."

When, after heroic efforts, the letter was finished, Theodosia carried it to her mother's sitting room. Mrs. Burr was seated in a low armchair by the fire. She looked rested and refreshed, and a warm smile lighted her face as she heard Theodosia's account of the afternoon. Mrs. Burr shared her husband's firm belief in the right of every young person to be educated, and it was a household rule that every servant, whether free or slave, must be taught at least to read or write.

"You did very well, dear," Mrs. Burr said, when she had glanced through the blotted little message to Lottie's mother, concealing a smile here and there at oddly turned phrases and quaint misspellings. "I had meant to see to Lottie's instruction myself, as soon as I was able, but since you have begun the task so bravely, you may try the lesson each afternoon. Your papa will be pleased I know."

Peggy brought in buttered crumpets with tea, and Theodosia munched hungrily in spite of her afflicted jaw. By the time John came home from his fencing lesson, her spirits were remarkably revived. When he offered to show her the new fencing maneuver he had learned that afternoon, she lunged at him so eagerly that he drew back, looking quite alarmed.

"Slowly, Theo, slowly," he warned her. "We're not supposed to kill each other!"

## ·CHAPTER 5·

# The Shadows Pass

THE NEXT SUMMER in Pelham was a quiet one for Theodosia. John was away a good deal, having begun his apprenticeship in reading law with Mr. Burr. Mrs. Burr grew gradually weaker and she spent the long days on the veranda, sewing or resting while she looked out over the orchard toward the sunlit shore.

To Theodosia and Frederic fell the responsibility of managing the household and the farm. Frederic took over the outdoor work while Theodosia helped to supervise the domestic affairs. Peggy and Anthony and the other servants found their young mistress surprisingly capable at planning meals, ordering supplies, and generally keeping track of the house.

Each week Theodosia drove into the village with Anthony to visit the shops, and by the end of the summer she was an expert marketer, able to select at a glance the best cut of beef, the freshest vegetables, and the plumpest chickens.

Shopkeepers who had treated her with patronizing indulgence at first, soon learned that their young customer had a sharp eye and no intention of being cheated, and before long they were striving as hard to please her critical taste as though she had been a grand lady instead of a little girl of ten.

When Papa came to stay, he found Theodosia able to give him a complete report on her mother's health. They talked a good deal together during the summer visits, taking long walks in the afternoons while Mrs. Burr napped. More and more Mr. Burr began to treat his daughter as an equal.

At the close of summer, it was decided that Frederic would remain at Pelham. Having tried to study law, and found it not to his taste, Frederic had decided to take up farming. So the Pelham house and the surrounding acres were formally deeded to him.

It was a sad wrench for them all when the time came to leave, and Frederic, his bronzed young face very sober, watched the carriage down the drive until a bend in the road hid the last glimpse of Theodosia's sunbonnet, waved in lingering farewell.

John was to be with Mr. Burr in Philadelphia for the winter, so only Mrs. Burr and Theodosia were left in Richmond Hill, and the big house seemed more empty and filled with echoes than ever.

But Theodosia had no long idle hours in which to contemplate her lonely state. There was responsibility to be shouldered, and Theodosia, feeling herself a young woman now, went at her tasks willingly. Papa depended on her—and she was determined not to fail him.

Instead of the playful little notes they had exchanged in

the preceding winter, Mr. Burr expected long, careful letters from Theodosia, giving reports of her mother, household news, and an account of her own activities and studies.

Mr. Burr answered with equal care. Never, on any account, he wrote, was *anything* to interfere with Theo's studies. On that point he was adamant. So Theodosia worked faithfully, and when she managed to bring her lessons up to his expectations, he gave her such generous praise and encouragement that she was fired with new ambition.

It was in March that Mrs. Burr's long illness became more grave. Less than a month later, when the willows that fringed the garden she loved so well had just begun to show the shadowy green of a new spring, she died.

Until the very end Mrs. Burr had refused to allow her illness to interfere with her husband's career. In spite of his frequent protests that he must resign from Congress to be at home with her, she had kept on so cheerfully, and endured her sufferings with such patience that he had yielded to her wishes and remained at his work.

It was typical of Aaron Burr's philosophy that, once the beloved presence of his wife had vanished from Richmond Hill, his letters to Theodosia made no reference to the loss. And so thoroughly had his daughter already been disciplined in his iron school of accepting the inevitable without lament that she also refrained from the slightest hint of grief in her answers. The letters that passed between them in the months following Mrs. Burr's death were full of news, affectionate pleasantries, and plans for the future, unshadowed by their knowledge that the close family circle, which had meant so much to them both, was now sadly shattered.

Nevertheless, the problem of his young daughter's loneliness concerned Mr. Burr deeply, and one day Theodosia was startled out of her mood of languid boredom by a letter from Papa which announced a new and charming plan.

A young French girl, Natalie de L'age, was to come to Pelham as Theodosia's guest for the summer. And, wrote Papa, Miss Theo would please to stir herself out of the doldrums and make every effort to make her guest's visit a pleasant one.

Nothing could have delighted Miss Theo more. Her natural good spirits returned with a rush, and by the time Natalie arrived her young hostess was waiting eagerly, with a dozen plans for picnics, horseback rides, and boating trips already arranged.

Natalie had been for some time a protégée of Mr. Burr. His theories about education had often led him to undertake the training and encouragement of youngsters who, by unusual talents and intelligence, attracted his attention. He had, indeed, a continual succession of boys and girls under his wing—and he contributed to their education with reckless generosity and his usual cheerful disregard of his already mountainous debts.

Natalie and Theodosia got on beautifully from the start. They were almost the same age and both girls liked riding and dancing and parties quite as much as they did reading and study. Before the summer was out they were dreading the time when they must separate, and great was their delight when Mr. Burr wrote that Mme. de L'age, who was returning to France for the winter, would allow Natalie to stay on at Richmond Hill.

As it turned out, Natalie's mother prolonged her stay in France for several years. So Natalie slipped easily into the family circle. The two girls were like sisters and Mr. Burr played papa to his pretty daughters with impartial devotion.

Soon Mr. Burr was bringing visitors home with him and the grace and liveliness of the two young hostesses of Richmond Hill charmed his most distinguished guests. There were luncheons and teas and dinner parties, and the big house that had been so long quiet rang once more with the laughter and voices of company.

Travelers from abroad came to dine frequently. M. Talleyrand was often there from France, and he was always delighted when the two girls chatted with him as easily and wittily in French as they did in English.

Jerome Bonaparte, the younger brother of Napoleon, was another guest from France. His darkly aristocratic good looks and elegant manners enchanted the girls.

"*Mon Dieu*," Natalie sighed to Theodosia after young Bonaparte's first visit, "*qu'il est beau, cet jeune homme!* Don't you wish, Theo, that we were older? Perhaps he might fall in love with one of us."

Theodosia smiled at Natalie, curled up in a big chair before the bedroom fire. "He is nice," she agreed. "All the same, I don't mean to fall in love with anyone."

Natalie sat up. "But what then, Theo? You surely don't want to be an old maid, do you?"

Theodosia shrugged. "I shouldn't mind so long as I can stay with Papa, and keep house for him. Later, he says, I can travel with him wherever he goes."

Natalie shook her head. "Papa won't want an old maid for a daughter, I can tell you that," she said wisely. "And for all your high and mighty airs, Theo-mio, you'll change your mind quickly enough when you meet the right young man." .

On one late spring day, Theodosia and Natalie learned that President Washington, who was visiting in New York, had accepted an invitation to dine at Richmond Hill. The girls threw themselves into a fever of preparation. The carriage was ordered out and Anthony drove them into the city to market. There they roamed from stall to stall, inspecting the delicacies with anxious eyes, while all about them the vendors hawked their wares, so that the air rang with a weird medley of raucous, singsong cries:

"Sweet potatoes! Carolina potatoes! Here's your sweet Carolinas!"

"Any oranges, lemons, or limes today? Very fine, very cheap."

"Oysters, oysters. Here's your beauties of oysters! Here's your fine fat, salt oysters!"

Their marketing was finished at last and when they came back to Richmond Hill with the carriage loaded, Theodosia went into long, earnest conference with Peggy over the menu. They would have two kinds of soup. Then shad fresh from the Hudson, broiled over a charcoal fire and served with butter and wine. A mammoth turkey, pickled cucumbers, and fresh peas. Four kinds of preserves, and, for dessert, one of Peggy's famous almond puddings.

When the last detail was arranged, Theodosia flew upstairs to find Natalie putting the last touches to a centerpiece of flowers on the long dining table. There were pink roses and mignonette with tall spears of blue larkspur.

"Do you like it, Theo?" Natalie tipped her head to one side. "I mixed pink and blue especially since M. Bonaparte will be here and pink and blue is very French."

"It's lovely," Theodosia nodded. "Oh, and Natalie—*did* we remember to tell Lottie to lay out fresh linen upstairs?"

"Of course we did," Natalie answered soothingly. "Now do calm yourself, Theo, or you will explode altogether and Papa will have to explain to the President that his charming daughter is in fragments."

Evening came at last and Lottie helped the girls dress in their frocks of white India muslin, embroidered and ruffled, with short puffed sleeves. Theodosia wore cherry-red velvet ribbon about her slender waist, while Natalie's sash was pale blue satin.

At the sound of carriage wheels in the driveway, they ran down the broad staircase to find Mr. Burr waiting in the dining room.

As Anthony swung open the door to admit the first guests, Natalie squeezed Theodosia's hand and whispered a last warning not to worry. Everything was certain to go off smoothly.

And indeed it did.

Mr. Burr was an excellent host, witty and charming. Politics were forgotten, or at least not mentioned, for the evening. Even Mr. Hamilton who arrived as a guest, with his pretty wife, seemed in excellent spirits. To see him standing next to his host, no observer would have guessed that these two handsome and urbane gentlemen, talking amiably over their cups of Madeira punch, were probably the bitterest rivals in all New York.

As for President Washington, he appeared to enjoy himself thoroughly. Silent and rather austere at first, he warmed to the charming gaiety of his young hostesses and told them stories of the days when he had lived in this house, dined at this table, and, on one nearly tragic occasion, had narrowly escaped being poisoned by a British spy who had obtained work in the kitchens.

Toward the end of dinner, under cover of the general laughter and talk, M. Bonaparte spoke quietly to Mr. Burr. "Forgive me for asking," he said, "but is it true that you are not, after all, to be the next ambassador to France? I had understood it was all arranged for you to go—but only this evening I learned that another man has been appointed instead. How can this be so?"

Mr. Burr toyed with his fork for a moment. "The plans were made, yes. The President himself had told me that I was chosen. But"—he paused—"other influences interfered at the last moment."

M. Bonaparte frowned. "What a pity. Your appointment would have been quite perfect, I assure you, and what a success your charming daughters would have been in Paris. If I am not too impertinent, what are these *other influences* that could spoil such an excellent plan?"

"My friend Hamilton had different plans," Mr. Burr said quietly. His cryptic glance rested on Mr. Hamilton seated farther down the long table. "You see, M. Bonaparte, I had the misfortune to spoil a plan of Mr. Hamilton's once."

"But that"—the Frenchman spread his hands—"is a

purely personal consideration. Surely the President would not allow himself to be moved because *one man* objected?"

Mr. Burr smiled. "When that one man is Hamilton," he said, "it might as well have been a thousand who objected to my appointment."

Late that evening, when the guests had gone, Natalie came into Theodosia's room. "Well, it was a success, our party, wasn't it, Theo? Papa says you must have charmed the President by magic, for he's never been known to talk as much or smile as often as he did for you. And I saw M. Bonaparte looking at you more than once, my Theo."

When Theodosia made no answer, Natalie added slyly, "But, of course, I might have told him not to waste his glances, since you never intend to fall in love anyway."

"Well, perhaps not *ever,*" Theodosia admitted cautiously. "But certainly not for ages and ages. Papa says no woman ever knows her own mind before she's thirty, so I mean to wait until then at least."

"*Thirty!*" Natalie made a face of despair. "*Mon dieu!* At thirty one is already ancient. Papa must have been teasing."

"But listen, Natalie." Theodosia put down her brush. "Here's real news! Papa told me this evening that in the fall, when he goes to the Congress again, you and I are to go with him to Philadelphia. Just think, we'll be like real ladies with rooms of our own. What do you think of that?"

For the next hour the girls amused themselves by laying excited plans, punctuated by frequent bursts of smothered giggles, for the gay times they were to have as real young ladies in the capital.

## ·CHAPTER 6·

# The People's Party

ALAS FOR ALL the plans.

When autumn came, Mr. Burr found that he must plead a law case in Albany, and another in Washington, which would keep him traveling continually between Philadelphia and these two cities. So the girls were left at Richmond Hill until the cases should be finished. Then, Papa promised, he would send for them at once.

Theodosia was badly disappointed. After her father's departure, she sulked unhappily, neglected her studies, and was generally so disagreeable that even Natalie's good humor was exhausted.

One morning the girls were riding the new saddle horses that Mr. Burr had given them. In spite of the golden sunshine and the bright October woods, Theodosia refused to break her moody silence. At length Natalie spoke out.

"You'd better be careful, Theo," she warned sharply, "or you'll have us both in trouble. I heard Mr. Leshlie complain that your lessons get worse every day. If Papa hears that news it will be *pfft—au revoir* for Theo."

Theodosia gave her reins an impatient flip. "Lessons," she said bitterly. "I don't believe Papa cares two pins for me, but only for my lessons. Greek, history, geography, mathematics, music, writing, fencing, dancing . . ." She checked them off on her fingers. "Sometimes I feel like nothing more than a walking copybook. I think perhaps," she added darkly, "that I shall marry young after all. At least a husband wouldn't forever be going off for months and months and leaving me nothing to amuse myself with but lessons."

Whether Mr. Leshlie complained to Mr. Burr, or whether hints of discontent crept into Theodosia's own letters, it wasn't long before Miss Theo received a communication from her busy father in which he took time to point out, in no uncertain terms, the deficiencies in her behavior:

> . . . I am sorry, very sorry, that you are obliged to submit to some reproof. Indeed, I am afraid that your want of attention and politeness require it. . . . A moment's reflection will convince you that this conduct will naturally be construed into arrogance; as if you felt that all attention was due to you, and as if you felt above showing the least to anybody. . . . I believe you will in the future avoid it. Observe how Natalie replies to the smallest civility offered to her. . . .
>
> Receive with calmness every reproof, whether made kindly or unkindly; whether just or unjust. Consider within yourself whether there has been no cause for it. If it has been groundless and unjust, nevertheless . . . we must learn to bear these things; and, let me tell you, that you will always feel much better, much happier, for having borne with serenity the spleen of anyone, than if you had returned spleen for spleen.
>
> You will, I am sure, my dear Theodosia, pardon such two grave pages from one who loves you, and whose happiness depends very much on yours. Read it over twice.

Make me no promises on the subject. On my return, I shall see in half an hour whether what I have written has been well or ill received. If well, it will have produced an effect.

. . . I cannot add anything sprightly to this dull letter. One dull thing you will hear me repeat without disgust that

I am your affectionate friend,
A. Burr

Thus reminded of her faults, Theodosia did credit to her training and had the grace to mend her ways. For a time, indeed, she was an altogether model pupil, and the very next letter from Papa showed that he was aware of her efforts:

Three hundred and ninety-five lines of Greek, all your exercises, and all your music. Go on, my dear girl, and you will become all I wish. . . .

On one of his trips to Albany that winter, Mr. Burr stopped off at a blacksmith's shop on a country road near Kingston. One of his horses had lost a shoe, and while the blacksmith worked, Mr. Burr strolled up the road. Returning a few minutes later, he was surprised to find, drawn on the stable door, a charcoal sketch of his own carriage and horses. He examined the picture with interest. Even in the hasty drawing there was a dash and spirit that made him wonder who the artist might be. Mr. Burr glanced around and saw a boy, thin and rather pale, but with an alert eager look.

Mr. Burr beckoned. "Boy, do you know who drew this?"

"I did it, sir."

"Indeed?" Mr. Burr eyed him thoughtfully. The lad

was dressed in a rough homespun shirt and trousers that dangled loosely about his thin legs. "And where did you learn to draw so well?"

"Nowhere, sir." The boy shook his head. "I live on a farm up the road a piece, and I'm apprenticed to the smithy here. But I like drawing pictures for fun—specially of horses."

Mr. Burr considered the sketch a moment longer, then he took a scrap of paper from his pocket and scribbled a few lines on it. "What's your name, boy?"

"John Vanderlyn."

"Very well, Vanderlyn." Mr. Burr handed over the paper with a smile. "Keep this. You're too bright a lad to be a blacksmith's apprentice forever. If the time comes when you'd like to see the world and learn to be a real artist, put a clean shirt in your pocket and come to this address I've written for you."

It was several months later that Mr. Burr, being home at Richmond Hill for a few days, was surprised at breakfast one morning by a small paper parcel that Anthony laid on the table before him.

"A boy brought this to the door, sir, and is waiting outside. He said you'd know when you opened it who he was."

Mr. Burr unwrapped the neat bundle and found a coarse, country-made, clean shirt inside, with a bit of paper tucked into the folds. It was the message, in his own handwriting, that he had given the blacksmith's boy on the country road near Kingston.

The lad was shown in at once, and welcomed. Within

a few days young Vanderlyn had been outfitted in city clothes, and was apprenticed to study drawing with one of Mr. Burr's artist friends in New York. So Mr. Burr had acquired still another protégé to educate, one whose talents and lively intelligence bade fair to make him a promising investment.

Even though the girls were left at Richmond Hill for the greater part of that year, there were still plenty of visitors.

One guest who was a great favorite was Dolley Madison. She had only recently been married to James Madison. Before that she had been a young widow with two small children and Mr. Burr had been the children's guardian.

"People may say unkind things about your papa sometimes," Mrs. Madison said to Theodosia one day. "I dare say sooner or later you'll begin to hear them. They say he's too extravagant—and always head over heels in debt. They may be right, but always remember, as I do, that much of his extravagance comes from helping other people. And he's as generous with his time and his friendship as he is with money. I shan't ever forget all his kindnesses to my children and me when we were left alone. He's the most unselfish friend I've ever had. I hope I may pay him back someday."

Theodosia and Natalie loved to listen to Dolley Madison's lively stories. "You wouldn't believe how different things were when I was growing up," she told the girls. "I was never allowed to dance or have music lessons, or so much as look at a boy. As for horseback riding or going on a picnic —such things would have been thought far too unladylike. My mother was so afraid the sun would ruin my complexion that she used to send me to school in long white cotton gloves with a muslin mask sewed under the brim of my sunbonnet to keep me from getting freckled."

"You must have looked like a little ghost," Theodosia said sympathetically. "Didn't you have any fun at all?"

"Well, not very much." Mrs. Madison shook her pretty head ruefully. "But I used to think when I grew up, and could do as I pleased, I'd learn to dance and play the piano and be the greatest flirt that ever lived." She laughed. "My husband says at least part of my wish has come true—though he'll never tell which part!"

In 1797, Mr. Burr's six-year term in the Senate came to an end. He ran for re-election, but was defeated. As usual he took his disappointment calmly. "After all," he observed to Theodosia on his return to Richmond Hill, "Heaven helps those who help themselves. With Hamilton exerting himself *against* my election so much more zealously than I worked *for* it—it's natural Heaven should have been on his side."

But although Mr. Burr was temporarily out of the political picture, he and Thomas Jefferson remained the leaders of the growing Democratic-Republican Party. The new party was the people's party and as they began to take a more and more active part in the government of their new nation, they rallied to the men who, they felt, represented them, rather than to the small and exclusive group of property owners who controlled the Federalist policies.

For years New York had been governed by a closed corporation of the best families—the Schuylers, the Clintons, the De Puysters, the Livingstons. Although Mr. Burr belonged with this group by birth and breeding and his own wealth and social position, his affiliation with the people's party threw him in direct opposition to those who had been his closest friends. There were those who felt that Aaron Burr's championing of the people's cause was nothing more than a trick for getting himself into high office. But Mr. Burr refused to take his political position too seriously. He went serenely on his way and never troubled to protest the charges of the Federalists, led by Hamilton, who called him a rabble-rouser.

Theodosia, however, was often troubled by the situation. She had always been a favorite with her father's friends, and they were the very people who now denounced Mr. Burr, even though they continued to invite his daughter to their homes and make a great pet of her. "It worries me, Papa," she complained one day, "to have people so kind to me when I know they're unkind to you."

Mr. Burr smiled. "They're not in the least unkind to me, dear Theo," he said easily. "They merely dislike some of my ideas. Which is no reason why they should dislike you, or you them. Treat them as your friends—which they are; avoid the subject of politics, and if they should happen to say something ill-natured about your papa, give them your most amiable smile and turn the conversation to the weather. In that way you will keep your own dignity, without, I assure you, harming mine in the slightest."

Talking to Natalie later, however, Theodosia sighed. "I do wish we could go on as we are now—with Papa just a plain lawyer again—and not have to worry about politics and people being rivals and hating each other."

"Perhaps you'll get your wish, Theo, but I doubt it."
Natalie shook her head. "John says he believes the new party
will win the next election, and if they do, Papa is quite likely
to be the President. So what would you think of that?"

"Oh, dear, I don't know." Theodosia sighed again and
ruffled her curls until they stood on end. "I'd be fearfully
proud of him, of course, and it *would* be fun living in the
President's house. But sometimes I think I'd rather belong
to a family without any ambitions at all."

The following year, Mr. Burr was elected to the New
York State Legislature. Once more the girls were left to keep
house at Richmond Hill while he attended the sessions in
Albany. But though political affairs and ambitions were
drawing him more and more into the public spotlight, Mr.
Burr always found time to be interested in the smallest details
of Theodosia's life at home. No matter how busy he was,
he managed to write to her by every post, long, detailed letters, in his most charming style, which commented on the
latest entries in her weekly journal, the progress of her studies,
her health, her household problems, and her amusements.

Those who regarded Aaron Burr as an ambitious
schemer, who cared for nothing in the world but his own
success, might have been surprised to read some of the letters
that went to Theodosia.

> Your being in the ballette charms me (*he wrote once*).
> If you are to practice on Wednesday evening, do not stay
> away for the expectation of receiving me. If you should
> be at the ballette, I will go forthwith to see you. *Adieu,
> chère fille.* . . .

## ·CHAPTER 7·

# The Locket

O N THE MORNING of her seventeenth birthday, Theodosia wakened early. Lying still for a moment, she
frowned at the unfamiliar sloping ceiling above her head
. . . then she remembered. She was in Albany, of course. In
a room at Witbeck's Tavern.

She and Natalie had arrived from Richmond Hill the
night before for a visit. They had found the rooms pleasant
and cheerful, with everything arranged for their comfort.
There was a fire on the hearth, a maid appeared with jugs
of hot water, and beside each place on the supper table they
had found a nosegay of bright flowers and a note from Mr.
Burr.

He was sorry not to welcome them in person, being
detained by business, but would they be pleased to appear
promptly at breakfast the next morning where he would
be waiting to see them? In a postscript he added that a
dancing party had been arranged for the evening following,
in honor of Theodosia's birthday.

Theodosia pushed back the covers and rose to open the shutters. She drew a deep breath of the mild June air. In the town square, the old elms spread their green branches as though each leaf had taken on new freshness from the morning sun. Here and there, on the grass, cobwebs glistened like round, pale moons.

"Happy birthday, Theo," Natalie called from the doorway.

"Oh, Natalie"—Theodosia raised her arms to stretch delightedly—"isn't it a gorgeous day? Do you suppose we could get Papa to hire some horses and go riding with us after breakfast?"

"I shouldn't be surprised. But we'll have to hurry to meet Papa downstairs. Lottie just came to tell me that he is waiting. And, Theo, Lottie says Papa told her he has a young gentleman to take you to the party tonight, with John and me. His name is Vanderlyn."

"Vanderlyn?" Theodosia turned. "Oh, of course, the country boy who wanted to be an artist. He came to Richmond Hill one morning with a clean shirt done up in a paper parcel."

Natalie nodded. "Well, it seems the country boy is quite grown up and elegant now," she said. "He studied painting with Gilbert Stuart and then Papa sent him to Paris last winter. Lottie says she saw him last night and he's *very* handsome."

Mr. Burr greeted the girls in the dining room downstairs, then he inspected them with a critical eye. "You both look charming," he said, smiling. "The picture of health and the mirror of fashion. Here—sit down. I've sent the coffee out to be kept hot for you."

All through the meal the girls talked continually, interrupting each other to tell Mr. Burr the latest news and ask a dozen questions about the dancing party.

Presently Mr. Burr took a small, flat parcel from his pocket, and laid it next to Theodosia's plate.

"A little birthday gift for Theo," he said, "in the hope that she will wear it tonight and be as happy as her presence makes me."

He spoke lightly, but there was a look of tender pride in his eyes as he watched his daughter's pretty face bend eagerly over the package.

"Oh, Papa!" Theodosia opened the satin case. "Papa— it's *beautiful!*" She lifted a narrow black velvet ribbon from which hung a locket of delicate, chased gold, set with a filigree of pearls and emeralds. "See, Natalie, how well it will go with my new frock." She held the slender ribbon against her throat and looked up to meet her father's glance. "Papa, I do thank you a *thousand* times."

"One will be enough." Mr. Burr smiled. "It suits you very well, I think. I had Vanderlyn order it for me in Paris —and though he hasn't seen you since you were a little girl, my description of your devastating beauty must have been accurate—for he's chosen the very thing. Don't you agree, Natalie?"

Natalie nodded. She reached for the locket and opened the catch to show a small, glass-covered frame inside.

"What shall you put here, Theo?" she asked teasingly.

"It should be a lock of her true love's hair, shouldn't it, Papa?"

"And high time she had a true love, too," he agreed, still smiling. "Mind you find her one at the party tonight."

John came in, and there was another round of greetings.

"You've got fat, John," Theodosia eyed her brother critically. "That's what comes of reading too much law and not exercising enough."

"I follow Father's example," John said amiably, "and no one could accuse *him* of being plump!"

"Papa doesn't have your weakness for plum cakes and honey buns." Theodosia laughed. "But never fear, Natalie and I will take you in hand. To start things off, I propose a horseback ride this morning."

"No sooner said than done," John said. "I shall order the horses at once and select a particularly mean-tempered beast for you, Theo-mio, to pay you back for your remarks about my figure. You'll come with us, won't you, Father?"

Mr. Burr shook his head regretfully.

"I'm afraid not this time," he said, drawing out his watch. "There's an appointment I must keep. But I expect Vanderlyn will be happy to take my place."

"He certainly will," John agreed. "Poor Vanderlyn has heard so much about the fatal charms of these two young ladies that he's half smitten with them both sight unseen. I'll go and call him, and we'll meet in half an hour. . . . Mind you're prompt now," he called after Theodosia and Natalie as they hurried upstairs, "or Vanderlyn is likely to swoon away altogether with the strain of anticipation."

Later, as they guided their horses through the cobbled city streets and into a narrow lane that twisted and turned up the wooded hillside, they rode two and two. John and Natalie went ahead, and the sound of their voices drifted back through the clear, sunlit air as they chatted gaily.

For a while Theodosia and her companion rode in silence. Mr. Vanderlyn had grown from the awkward country boy she remembered into a quiet, serious sort of young man, not in the least given to the kind of nonsense that John was forever prattling. It was true, as Lottie had said, that Mr. Vanderlyn was handsome. Theodosia liked the way he rode, with an easy control of his horse.

Presently, turning to speak, Theodosia found her companion looking directly at her with a thoughtful expression in his eyes.

"You look very sober, Mr. Vanderlyn," she said. "Shall I offer you a sixpence for your thoughts?"

"I was just thinking how different you are from what I imagined, Miss Theodosia. I'd heard so much about you from your father—I really expected to be quite terrified by you. I thought you'd be most frightfully learned!"

Theodosia laughed. "I dare say Papa's descriptions make me sound awful, though I'm sure he means them well. He's spent so much time trying to make me a truly educated female that I suppose people expect me to be spouting Latin phrases and quoting obscure passages of Greek at every turn in the conversation. And instead——" She paused and shrugged.

"Instead, I find you very friendly and charming—and not in the least terrifying."

"Thank you, sir." Theodosia smiled at him with candid pleasure. "If another young man had said that, I should think it was only a pretty speech. But since you are a protégé of Papa's—and I know how thoroughly he detests flattery—I take you at your word, Mr. Vanderlyn."

"Good. I see there are even more advantages than I had thought in being one of your father's protégés. You know," he added soberly, after a moment, "there have been times when I've almost wished Mr. Burr hadn't as much faith in my talents as he appears to have. I'm no end grateful for all he's done for me, of course, but all the same it's a great responsibility. I feel that I *must* succeed in being a good painter, if only to show him that his encouragement hasn't been altogether misplaced. And yet I wonder sometimes if I ever can. He seems to expect so much of the people he believes in."

"Oh, I know," Theodosia said quickly. "I feel the same way often. I think the trouble is that Papa judges us all by himself. He thinks we should be as strong as he is, and he doesn't realize that sometimes we just aren't."

"It's odd, though, how hard we'll try," Vanderlyn said. "I remember talking to a young lawyer in your father's office one day. He said, 'I owe everything I have to Mr. Burr. He gave me my education and taught me all I know, but I'm most grateful for the way he's made me learn to depend on myself. *He made me iron.*' I suppose it's that quality in Mr. Burr that makes people either admire him so much or else mistrust him altogether."

"I suppose so," Theodosia agreed with a little sigh. "But I'm not altogether sure, Mr. Vanderlyn, that I *want* to be iron. It doesn't sound like a particularly comfortable thing to be."

When they came back for lunch, Vanderlyn helped Theodosia dismount and took her arm with a confidential smile.

"You won't tell your father that I may not turn out to be another Michelangelo after all, will you, Miss Theo?"

"Not a word, Mr. Vanderlyn. And you must never breathe to a soul that I didn't fire a single Latin phrase at you. Agreed?"

"On my solemn oath!"

They parted laughing, as Theodosia gathered up her long black skirt to run lightly up the steps after Natalie.

## CHAPTER 8

# The Third Waltz

WHEN THEODOSIA CAME down dressed for the party that evening, her dark curls were piled high on her head, and her bright coloring and slim, graceful figure were set off to perfection by the pale green of her watered-silk frock. At her throat she wore the new locket on its narrow black band, and Vanderlyn's smile lighted with pleasure as he saw it.

"How well the locket suits you, Miss Theodosia," he said. "You've no idea how I prowled through the shops in Paris trying to find just the very thing for you. I must admit I think I chose well."

Theodosia touched the locket lightly, and answered his look of frank admiration with a little curtsy. But Natalie, coming down just then, reached out to tap Vanderlyn's arm with her fan.

"Theodosia won't flirt with you, I warn you, M. Vander-lyn," she said. "So save your pretty speeches for a head more easily turned than hers."

"Like yours, for instance?" John asked.

Natalie nodded complacently, as she linked her arm in John's. She wore a frock of light yellow that brought out the delicate ivory tints of her skin, and in her dark hair she had pinned a cluster of tiny yellow rosebuds.

"Like mine," she agreed. "For you can be sure, M. Vanderlyn, that I get no overdose of compliments from John, who still scolds and teases me as if I were a naughty little girl in pigtails."

Coming into the candlelit, flower-decked rooms filled with people, Theodosia was instantly surrounded by friends, young and old. Their voices, gay and eager, rang about her, as, smiling, she greeted one after another.

"Theo, my dear, here's someone who's very anxious to meet you—a friend of your father's." Theodosia turned to find her hostess and a tall, broad-shouldered gentleman at her elbow.

"Mr. Joseph Alston," her hostess said, and, looking up, Theodosia found herself smiling into a pair of eyes, deep-set and extraordinarily blue. She felt her hand clasped for a moment in a warm, firm grip.

"Mr. Alston is from South Carolina," the hostess went on. "He's been in Albany on business, but now he claims he must go home again, which is altogether tiresome of him. See if you can't persuade him that there's far more to be said for a summer in the North than in the South, Miss Theodosia. If you succeed, I assure you every young lady in town will bless your name."

She turned away then and Theodosia found that she was still looking straight into Mr. Alston's eyes.

"It's rather a tall order I've been given, I'm afraid," she said. "But let's see—how shall I tempt you with the advantages of the North, Mr. Alston? Shall I tell you that we have excellent libraries? Or that our public parks are noted for their beauty? Or are you interested in birds, by any chance? Because if you are, we have some of the rarest specimens to be found——" She broke off suddenly with a laugh. "Really, Mr. Alston, I don't believe you're listening to me at all."

"Oh, but I am, Miss Burr. I was drinking in every word, but at the same time I was thinking of something that would tempt me more than libraries or parks or even rare specimens of birds." His blue eyes crinkled with amusement.

"Name it, Mr. Alston. If Albany possesses it, it shall be yours."

"I was thinking I should like very much to have a dance with you, Miss Burr. Unless the young gentleman you came in with has already claimed them all. In which case, I promise you, I shall set out for South Carolina this very instant, and I shouldn't be at all surprised if I drove so recklessly that I broke my neck."

"Oh, let's prevent that, by all means, Mr. Alston. Would the third waltz be sufficient to keep you from an untimely end, do you think? Or would you prefer a polka?"

"I'd prefer both," said Mr. Alston promptly.

Next morning at breakfast the talk was all of the party. Natalie and John exchanged opinions about this person and that, but Theodosia sat silent for the most part, breaking a piece of bread into a little heap of crumbs beside her plate.

"It's such a pity Mr. Alston must leave today, isn't it, Papa?" Natalie asked presently.

"You liked him then?"

"Oh, yes, ever so much. Didn't you, Theo?"

"Didn't I what, Natalie?" Theodosia looked up with a start.

Natalie laid down her fork. *"Didn't—you—like—Mr.— Alston?"* she repeated, exaggerating each syllable carefully.

"Oh"—Theodosia dropped her glance again—"why, yes —I thought he was very nice."

John and Natalie exchanged a quick glance, and Natalie shrugged lightly. "I think, Papa," she said, "that our Theo is in such a state of cloudy dreams this morning she seems scarcely able to recall meeting anyone."

As they were finishing their coffee, Lottie came into the dining room with a note for Theodosia. A man was waiting for an answer, she said.

Theodosia stared at her name written in a firm, slanting script as though she couldn't quite believe what she saw. Then she broke the seal. As she read, a curious change came over her face. She looked up with eyes grown oddly bright, and though she spoke quietly, there was a breath of eagerness beneath her words.

"Mr. Alston has changed his plans, Natalie. He won't be leaving today after all! He wants to know if we'll ride with him this morning. Shall I say yes?"

"Of course, if you like."

"Then I'll go." Theodosia jumped up. "And you'll go with us, won't you, Papa?"

When Mr. Burr shook his head, Theodosia made a little

pout of impatience. *"Please,* papa! we won't have half the
fun without you, and Mr. Alston will be disappointed, I'm
sure."

"I dare say Mr. Alston will survive his disappointment."
Mr. Burr smiled pleasantly enough, but as he watched his
daughter run quickly out to give her message, a curious look
came into his eyes, as though something had suddenly surprised him, and the lines about his chin grew firm, even
though he kept on smiling.

The last bright days of June melted into July and the
Hudson Valley sweltered in the summer heat. Mr. Burr was
detained in Albany from week to week, by his work and
by a number of visitors who came to confer with him over
the approaching elections.

For once Theodosia appeared not to mind the hot
weather. She lingered on in the capital, saying merely that
she would rather stay until her father's work was finished.

Somehow, mysteriously, Mr. Alston's business in Albany
prolonged itself also. He, like Theodosia, seemed to thrive
on the long hot days.

Most of Theodosia's friends had closed their houses and
gone to the mountains or the seashore, but though there
were no more parties, she and Natalie still found plenty
to do. They rode in the early mornings now, through deep-
shaded trails where the air was still cool and fresh from the
dew that sparkled in the long grass beside the path. And in
the evenings, there were picnics or sailing parties on the
river.

Gradually Mr. Alston came to be included in their plans

as a matter of course. He rode well, cheerfully undertook a good share of the work on picnic suppers, and was an accomplished sailor. More and more his name began to be taken for granted in the family conversations.

Only Theodosia remained perversely silent on the subject of the tall, broad-shouldered young man with the deep-set blue eyes.

On one Sunday morning in the middle of July, Mr. Burr had to visit a client in Schenectady. He suggested that the young people drive over with him. At the last moment Natalie developed a headache. So it happened that while Mr. Burr and John were at their client's house, Theodosia was left with Mr. Alston. It was a pleasantly cool day, and when they had finished dinner, they left the carriage at the inn and started out for a walk through the Sunday quiet of the elm-shaded streets.

They talked amiably enough of this and that, but presently there was a silence, and Theodosia looked up to find Mr. Alston smiling at her in a curious way.

"Do you realize, Miss Theodosia, that this is the first time you and I have been alone together since we've met?"

"Is it, Mr. Alston?"

"It is, Miss Theodosia. And what's more, I think you're quite as well aware of it as I."

"We've all been together so much——"

"Not so much but what you have plenty of time to talk with Vanderlyn."

"Mr. Vanderlyn likes to talk to me about his work."

"Oh! . . . Then I'm afraid you won't have very much to say to me, since I have no work to talk about."

Theodosia looked up seriously. "Don't you do anything at all, Mr. Alston?"

"Not very much. My father left me a great many rice fields, in South Carolina, but the plantation manager looks after those a good deal better than I could. Besides, I don't suppose you'd care to talk about rice fields; there isn't much to say about them except that they're damp and full of mosquitoes."

"I thought I heard Papa say one time that you'd taken a degree in law, Mr. Alston?"

"So I did." He nodded cheerfully. "But the law and I didn't seem to take to each other very well, so I haven't done much about it."

They walked in silence for a few minutes, then Mr. Alston asked curiously, "Is that why you disapprove of me, Miss Theodosia? Because I have no work to talk about?"

"I don't disapprove of you, Mr. Alston."

"But you don't approve of me either. And I approve of you so very much. You've no idea how many hours I've spent wondering what it was about me that didn't please you. Doesn't that make you feel a little sorry for me, Miss Theo?"

"Not in the least," she said, and they both laughed.

After a little they wandered into a park and sat down on a bench facing a pond where two white swans glided sedately about, nibbling at the shrubs and grass along the water's edge. Theodosia took off her wide-brimmed hat and let the light wind ruffle her curls.

"You know, Miss Theodosia," Mr. Alston went on after a few minutes, "I think you might at least tell me what it is you don't like about me."

"And what then, Mr. Alston?" Theodosia leaned down to scoop up a handful of pebbles and tossed them into the water, one by one. "Would you set about to change yourself?"

"Not at all," he said calmly. "I should merely try to convince you that they aren't such bad qualities after all."

"But I'm an extraordinarily difficult person to convince, Mr. Alston."

"And I'm extraordinarily persistent, Miss Theodosia." Theodosia tossed the last pebble away and stood up.

"So I'm beginning to think," she said, and smiled as she took his arm.

As the days went on, Mr. Burr observed his daughter without comment. Never had he seen her looking prettier, nor in better spirits. But still she said nothing about Mr. Alston.

There was a night when they all went sailing on the river by the light of a full, bright moon. Suddenly a mutter of thunder rolled over the hills on the west bank, and within a few moments the moon was blacked out and a sharp wind whipped the river into gusty, squalling waves.

Mr. Alston shouted directions to John and Vanderlyn as they struggled with desperate haste to lower the canvas that cracked like pistol shots in the angry wind. Hurry as they might, they barely succeeded in lowering the last of the sails in time to prevent the gusts of wind from capsizing the boat.

They drifted on the black water, heaved this way and that by the waves, while flash after flash of lightning split the darkness and the thunder rolled and echoed between the riverbanks with deafening crashes.

When the storm was spent, and they were safe, the men managed to maneuver the limping, half water-logged boat to shore, and through a drenching rain the party climbed the hill from the landing back to town.

Mr. Alston walked beside Theodosia. His coat had been lost overboard, and his shirt was torn, leaving one shoulder half bare. He had had no chance to speak to Theodosia while they were in the boat, but now he looked down at her, drenched and shivering at his side.

"Are you all right, Miss Theo?"

She glanced up quickly. "Quite all right, Mr. Alston."

"You were so calm while we were out there. Tell me honestly, weren't you the least bit frightened?"

"Not particularly," she said.

"But most young ladies I know would have been terrified," he insisted. "They would have had hysterics, or fainted, or at the very least set up a howl because their frocks were ruined. Yet you and Miss Natalie were quite calm."

Theodosia laughed. "The young ladies you know weren't brought up by Aaron Burr, Mr. Alston. Ever since I can remember, Papa has taught us not to be afraid of things. Even when I was a little girl, and hated the dark, he'd never let Nanny leave a light in my room."

"Weren't you frightened of the dark just the same?"

"Oh, yes, more than ever. But I soon learned not to show it, for when I cried, Papa was disappointed in me and that was even worse. You mustn't think I'm especially brave, Mr. Alston, because I'm not. It's easy not to let yourself be frightened of thunderstorms and the dark and such things, but I *am* afraid sometimes of other things."

"What things, Miss Theodosia?" he asked gently.

She was silent for a moment, then shook her head without answering him. She couldn't explain, really, so anyone would understand, about the odd little corners of loneliness in her heart, where it seemed sometimes as if a tiny, faint bell were sounding, even in moments of happiness, a far-off note of warning. She couldn't explain how she was afraid sometimes for Papa—and the queer dread she had of leaving him, as though, if she weren't there, something terrible was sure to happen.

Theodosia sighed, and the sigh ended in a little shivering breath. In the darkness beside her, Mr. Alston said nothing. But she felt his hand on her arm, warm and sure and strong. And somehow understanding.

A few days later Mr. Burr's business was finished, and they prepared to leave at once for Pelham. Mr. Alston was leaving the same day, he said, to start south.

On the last evening in Albany they rode up into the hills for a farewell picnic supper. Sitting around the fire afterward, they felt a little sad, and the conversation kept lagging into silence, until at last Natalie jumped up and said that everybody was being altogether too mournful.

"Anyone would suppose," she said, "that we were all going to the ends of the earth and would never see each other again. I vote we play charades."

They played for an hour or so, laughing a good deal in the process. If anyone noticed that Theodosia's acting was less spirited than usual and that Mr. Alston looked strangely abstracted, they said nothing of it.

Nor did the others appear to notice how silent Theodosia and Mr. Alston were during the ride home under the twilight sky, where the first stars hung pale and faintly glimmering. But when they had said good-by to Vanderlyn and Mr. Alston, Mr. Burr came into the small sitting room and found Theodosia standing alone by the window.

"Theo——"

She turned quickly. "Yes, Papa?"

"You're not sad—or troubled, are you, Theo?"

For an answer, she drew her locket from beneath the high white muslin stock of her riding habit. Opening the catch, she showed him the little frame, still empty.

He looked down into the clear, dark eyes that met his glance so honestly. "When the time comes, Theo, you are to think of yourself and your own happiness—not of any misguided notion of duty toward *me*. Will you remember that?" There was a note of sternness in his voice, as if, somehow, he had sensed the vague, nameless misgivings Theodosia felt for him—and rejected them.

She snapped the locket shut, and the catch made a small sound of finality in the quiet room.

"I must remember for a long time, then," she said, laughing a little ruefully. "Because in spite of Natalie's warnings, you'll have to learn to be content with an old maid daughter—whether you like it or no."

## ·CHAPTER 9·

# The Die Is Cast

B UT THEODOSIA HAD not reckoned on just *how* persistent Joseph Alston could be.

For the rest of the summer, and the early weeks of autumn, scarcely a post arrived from the South that didn't bring her a packet of letters from Charleston.

Miss Theodosia need not think, wrote Mr. Alston, that merely because they were now separated by a distance of more than seven hundred miles, he was any the less determined to discover her objections to him, and to overcome them.

Her objections, Miss Theodosia replied by the next post, were not toward Mr. Alston, for whom she held the highest regard, but toward the notion of marrying anyone, however charming and however *persistent.*

Marriage, Mr. Alston wrote, is a noble estate.

True, admitted Theodosia, but an estate she had no faintest intention of entering until she was of a sufficiently mature age to grace its nobility.

And what, pray, demanded Mr. Alston, did she consider a sufficiently mature age?

Thirty, at least, Theodosia stated flatly.

Absurd, said Mr. Alston.

Not at all, retorted Theodosia with spirit. Papa agreed with her that no girl of seventeen was possibly to be considered capable of making up her own mind.

Then why not, Mr. Alston suggested, let him make it up for her?

Most certainly *not,* the haughty Miss Burr replied.

And as for quoting her Papa's opinion, Mr. Alston added, it was a mistake indeed to think *that* bore any weight. Had he not asked and received Mr. Burr's consent to the match? And not so much as a word had Mr. B. uttered, not a syllable, to the effect that he considered his daughter too young to be married.

Silence from Theodosia.

No more letters from Charleston.

Three weeks passed, and no word.

And as post after post arrived from the South and still no letter from Joseph, the strong-minded Miss Theodosia began to show certain signs of weakening.

It was observed in the Burr household that Theo appeared to be suffering from a mysterious loss of appetite. Frequent fits of dreamy absent-mindedness made her quite oblivious to the mundane matters of daily living, and before the arrival of each post she was thrown into the most curious agitation, only to be followed by equally unaccountable fits of gloom.

In short, as Natalie observed to Mr. Burr, it was plain to be seen that Theodosia was in love.

"But, oh dear, *why* did she have to be so horrid to poor Mr. Alston?" Natalie sighed. "Now she's made him angry, and though *she's* sorry, *he* doesn't know it—and they're both too proud to write and give in. Why *does* love have to be so complicated and why does it make everyone miserable, Papa?"

Mr. Burr shook his head. "Being miserable is only one of the peculiar fascinations of being in love," he said. "Don't worry too much, Natalie. They're a stubborn pair, but I think in the end each will learn to give in to the other a bit —and likely each will feel noble and virtuous in the bargain."

Nevertheless, when the time came for Mr. Burr to leave Richmond Hill to attend the legislature, he was not altogether at ease about the state of his daughter's heart.

It was the autumn of 1800, and, true to John's prediction, the growing sentiment in favor of the new party made it seem certain that an Antifederalist would win the coming presidential election.

Burr and Jefferson were the most popular leaders of the new party. One of them, it was clear, was sure to succeed John Adams as the next President of the United States.

Electoral votes were cast. The result was a tie between Jefferson and Burr.

The Senate, in Philadelphia, must vote now, to resolve the tie.

John wrote from Albany that the result was a foregone conclusion. People were saying everywhere that Aaron Burr would be chosen.

The household at Richmond Hill was thrown into the greatest excitement. *Papa* was going to be President! John said so. John said *everybody* said so! It must be so.

Theodosia overcame her prejudices against politics and was thrilled by the prospect. She planned with Natalie what sort of dresses they would have for the inaugural ball. She conferred with Peggy about the wonderful dinners they would serve to the new President and his Cabinet. She even forgot, for a time, to languish over the post which still brought no letters from Charleston.

But in the meantime Mr. Hamilton had heard the news also. He had heard that *everyone* was saying the Senate was sure to decide the tie in favor of Burr. And that, for Mr. Hamilton, was enough. He went straight to Philadephia and set out, virtually singlehanded, to keep the Senate from electing Aaron Burr.

Never in all the years he had opposed Burr had his attack been so furious as now. He was sincerely convinced that the election of Aaron Burr would ruin the country, and he used every ounce of his influence to convince the Senate that this was so. He denounced Burr on every conceivable ground: political, personal, and moral. If his charges were untrue, then why was not Mr. Burr present to deny them? Where, indeed, demanded Hamilton, *was* Mr. Burr at this most important crisis of his life?

Why, Mr. Burr was in Albany.

And in Albany Mr. Burr remained, serenely unperturbed while the battle raged. Not once did he make a move to defend himself against the charges of Hamilton and the other Federalists, and no entreaties from his friends could move him from his policy of silence.

On the night when the news of the Senate's final vote reached Albany, it was raining. William Van Ness, a friend and loyal supporter of Mr. Burr, hurried to Witbeck's Tavern as quickly as he could, and found Mr. Burr alone in his sitting room.

"Mr. Burr," said Van Ness, "you have been defeated."

Mr. Burr looked up from his desk. "Have I?" he asked mildly.

Van Ness flung himself into a chair and leaned his head on his hands. "Jefferson is President," he said. "You'll be Vice-president."

Mr. Burr looked thoughtful for a moment, then he smiled.

"Don't take it too hard, Van Ness," he said. "Vice-president is much better than nothing." Noticing the dampness of his friend's coat, Mr. Burr said quickly, "Here, let me take your coat before you get chilled through. I'll send downstairs for a toddy for you."

Van Ness looked up. "Upon my word, Mr. Burr," he said slowly, "I don't know whether you're the greatest hero in this country—or the greatest fool."

The bland, enigmatic smile on Mr. Burr's face did not change as he spread the coat before the fire to dry. "I hardly think it likely," he said, "that I have the honor of being either."

"But surely you must realize"—the younger man leaned

forward earnestly—"that Hamilton alone is responsible for this. That he deliberately kept you from the presidency by denouncing you, slandering you, accusing you of every corruption under the shining sun. And yet you've refused to so much as raise a hand in your own defense. Even now, with the damage already done, you don't appear to *care,* sir—or you would——"

"I would what?" Mr. Burr, seated at his desk again, glanced up quickly. "What would you have me do, Van Ness? Give way to bad temper and challenge my friend Hamilton?"

"Duels have been fought for a great deal less, Mr. Burr."

"I expect that's true," Mr. Burr nodded. He picked up a round glass paperweight and held it a moment in silence, as though he were testing its weight. Then, replacing it carefully, he drew a sheet of paper toward him, and asked if Van Ness would do him the favor of dropping two letters in the post on his way home.

"I'd like to send congratulations to Mr. Jefferson," he said, "and I must write a little note to Theodosia. This news will be a disappointment to her, I'm afraid." For the first time Mr. Burr's voice showed a trace of concern. "Though I expect," he added, smiling, as he began to write, "she'll go to the greatest pains to conceal that fact from me."

## ·CHAPTER 10·

# Wedding Day

CHRISTMAS CAME AND WENT. Still there was no letter for Theodosia from Charleston.

Mr. Burr, home for the holidays, found his daughter in a mood that gave him fresh concern. Although she held to her stubborn pride and refused to mention the name of Joseph Alston, there was a new gentleness in her manner, and sometimes, as they sat around the study fire in the evenings, Mr. Burr observed that she was strangely silent, staring into the flames with a wistful longing in her eyes that went straight to his heart.

Meanwhile, in Charleston, Joseph was suffering precisely the same pangs of sadness and longing that plagued his Theodosia's lonely heart. It is hard to keep silent forever under such circumstances, pride or no pride, and Joseph wrote once again—a long, eloquent plea for the reconsideration of his cause that began, in peremptory and highhanded fashion: "Hear me, Miss Burr."

Because it was winter, and the roads were icy and travel-

66

ing difficult, the letter was a long while in reaching Theodosia. But there came a stormy evening, early in January, when Mr. Burr looked up suddenly to find Theodosia staring in silence at her dinner plate. He laid down his fork and took a deep breath.

"You're not wearing your locket tonight, Theo."

"No, Papa." Theodosia's voice was low, but quick color came into her cheeks. "I—put it away for a little while. It hasn't seemed right, somehow, to wear the locket. As long as it was empty, it was all right. But now . . ."

She paused and for a moment silence hung between them, broken only by the sound of the crackling fire. There was an odd expression on Mr. Burr's face; then, suddenly, he smiled.

"I wish you'd wear it again, Theo," he said. "And be happy."

Neither of them said anything more just then, but later that evening Theodosia went to her room and lifted the locket from its satin case. She watched the emeralds flash in the candlelight. Then, slipping the velvet ribbon over her head, she crossed quickly to the desk and sat down to write:

> My dear Joseph:
> I shall be very happy to see you whenever you choose; that, I suppose, is equivalent to very soon. . . . My father laughs at my impatience to see you, and says I am in love . . . *Adieu encore,*
>> Theodosia

Within a few hours after Theodosia's letter reached him, Joseph Alston was on his way north, and he made the long, difficult journey with such unprecedented speed that Mr. Burr declared he must have changed horses in every town along the way and driven the unhappy beasts into exhaustion in his impatience to reach Theodosia.

"And a good thing, too," Mr. Burr added. "For nothing in this world can change more quickly or unaccountably than a young lady's mind, Joseph—as you will doubtless have plenty of opportunities to learn."

But Theodosia, radiant and shining-eyed, showed not the slightest signs of wishing to change her mind again. She and Natalie plunged at once into plans for the wedding.

Everything had to be done quickly because both Theodosia and Joseph were anxious to be in Washington for the inauguration of Mr. Jefferson as President and Mr. Burr as Vice-president. It would be a small wedding, Theo decided. Natalie would be bridesmaid. In addition, only John and Frederic and Papa would be with them.

The night before the wedding the wind shifted to the west, and when Natalie came into Theodosia's room in the morning, she threw open the shutters to find that a heavy, silent snow was falling.

"Oh, Theo, do come and see how pretty it looks," Natalie said.

As the two girls stood together, arm in arm, looking out into the thickly swirling snow, Natalie turned suddenly. "Theo, whatever am I going to do without you?" she asked forlornly. "I've been so busy and excited about everything I hadn't stopped to think until this minute that you'll actually be gone. . . ."

"But not for long, Natalie," Theodosia answered quickly. "We'll all be together again in Washington in just a few weeks, and as soon as Joseph and I are settled in Charleston, you'll come to visit. Papa has promised to bring you, whenever he comes. And, Natalie"—for a moment the shining happiness in Theodosia's eyes clouded—"you *will* look after Papa, won't you? I . . ." She hesitated, leaving the words unfinished. Not even to Natalie could she speak of the vague, troubling fears for her father that haunted her so often.

There was a knock at the door, and Lottie came in with an armful of deep crimson roses. "Mr. Alston just brought these, Miss Theo," she said. Lottie was a grown woman now, tall and dignified, and very different from the gawky, lonely girl Theodosia had found in the little back room at Richmond Hill on a winter's afternoon long ago.

Taking the flowers, smiling into Lottie's eyes, Theodosia remembered that afternoon. And Lottie, looking back at the radiant face of her young mistress, remembered, too. "I do muchly hope you'll be very happy, Miss Theo," she said.

"Thank you, Lottie." Theodosia buried her face in the flowers, breathing the warm fragrance of the hothouse. "Oh, Lottie, I *am* so glad Papa says you can go south with Joseph and me. It'll seem like home to have you there."

She went to the bed where her wedding dress of creamy satin lay next to Natalie's rose-brocaded gown.

"See how lovely the roses look with our frocks, Natalie. We'll each carry an armful, and Joseph must have this one for his coat." She broke off a crimson bud and held the soft petals against her cheek for a moment.

It was a simple ceremony, and a pretty one. The curtains were drawn and lighted candles made a soft golden light over the greens and flowers banked before the fireplace where Joseph and Theodosia stood. Afterward there was a wedding breakfast, with champagne to toast the bride and groom, and when Theodosia started upstairs to change into her traveling suit, she paused for a minute on the stairs.

"Here," she cried. "The next bride must catch my bouquet." And she tossed the crimson roses straight into Natalie's arms.

When she said good-by to her father, Theodosia laid her cheek against the shoulder of his immaculate black coat, and for a moment she felt the quick, hot sting of tears.

"Papa—oh, Papa," she whispered.

Her father's arms held her gently. Then he drew back and touched the locket at her throat.

Instantly she straightened, and looked up with a smile as gallant and serene as his own.

"*Au revoir,* my Theo," he said.

"*Au revoir . . .*"

## ·CHAPTER 11·

# The Inaugural

THE NEXT THREE weeks were a sort of triumphal tour for the young Alstons. Traveling by easy stages, stopping here and there to visit friends on the way south, they were received everywhere with the most cordial hospitality. Dinners were given for them, balls and dances were arranged in their honor, and all who met them were delighted by the young couple who were so handsome, so gay, and so charmingly in love.

The days passed swiftly, in a round of visits and parties. All Theodosia's friends were anxious to meet her husband, and Joseph complained privately that he felt like a trained seal on exhibition.

"But such a very nice, superior trained seal, Joseph," Theodosia laughed. "They do approve of you quite thoroughly, you know. Even Mrs. Livingston told me she could almost understand my being willing to bury myself in the wilds of Carolina for the sake of such a handsome and accomplished husband as Mr. Alston."

It was the last day of February when the Alstons reached Baltimore. There they went directly to the inn where Mr. Burr and Natalie were to join them, and a letter from Papa was waiting for Theodosia. She read it eagerly, not stopping even to take off her cloak, and when she had finished she looked up at Joseph with shining eyes.

"It's all right, Joseph, they're really on the way, and expect to be here by the day after tomorrow. Oh, dear," she sighed in relief, "I've been *so* afraid something might happen to delay them."

Joseph bent to kiss her cheek, still cold and bright with color from the long drive in the winter's air. "Goose," he said affectionately. "What could possibly happen to keep your father from being present at his own inauguration? To say nothing of the fact that he's probably pining to see how married life agrees with you."

"Oh, I know." Theodosia smiled quickly. "It's foolish of me to worry. But it's so hard for me to remember that I'm not still a little girl who has to stay home alone when Papa's business keeps him away."

The next day Mr. Burr and Natalie arrived and they all drove to Washington together. Theodosia had her first taste of being a celebrity's daughter. People crowded about the carriage, eager for a glimpse of the new Vice-president and his family, and at every stopping place on the journey they found themselves surrounded.

Excitement ran high over the coming inaugural. The time had come now, people felt, when *they* were actually going to have a voice in the government. The new party was the people's party, and Mr. Jefferson was a President after their own hearts. No closed carriages for *him*—none of your pomp and ceremony and standing on official dignity. Here was a President who would ride his own horse or even walk alone in the streets. A President you could walk right up to and shake hands with, if you had a mind to. A man who looked and dressed and acted precisely like themselves.

It was too late now for the Federalists to do more than wag their heads despairingly. For the democratic spirit had caught the public fancy, and Thomas Jefferson was the man of the hour. To him the people gave a full measure of confidence and loyalty.

The new Vice-president was scarcely less popular. Aaron Burr might be a rich man, from a fine family, yet he wore a plain black coat and shook hands with anyone who wanted a word with him.

As for Theodosia, her presence in Washington put the finishing touch of popularity on the new administration. From the moment she stepped out of the carriage in front of Dolley Madison's house in Washington, where she and Joseph were to stay, the people loved her.

It was late in the afternoon when they arrived, and a raw spring rain was falling. But no sooner had the carriage drawn up at the curb than passers-by, hearing that the Vice-president's daughter was inside, gathered about, shivering in the damp air, to see her.

Even Joseph was surprised by the success of his wife's first public appearance. As she stepped down, slim and graceful in her long fur cloak and with a little feathered bonnet perched fashionably on her dark curls, the circle drew back for a moment, awed by the elegance of her dress and manner.

Theodosia hesitated, aware that in that moment the friendliness of her welcome was in doubt. Then an old woman pushed her way to the front of the group and Theodosia suddenly knew what to do. With a quick smile, she reached out and shook the old woman's hand.

"How do you do?" she said. "It's very kind of you to stop in all this rain to greet us."

The woman bobbed a curtsy, beaming with toothless pleasure at the honor of being singled out. "You're a pretty lass," she said, "and you've a fine young husband. God bless you both, ma'am, and your father and the new President too."

From that moment Theodosia had no further doubts about her welcome. The people crowded around with a good will, and for the next few minutes she and Joseph were kept busy shaking hands, while the rain still fell and the feather on her bonnet lost its stylish curl and hung limp and draggled against the wet shoulder of her cloak.

Never, after that, was Theodosia afraid of the crowds that followed her through the days before the inauguration. Although she found it not always to her liking to answer the questions of total strangers, who sometimes insisted on examining the material of her gowns with curious fingers, she bore herself with an easy dignity that won her friends everywhere.

Since Mr. Jefferson was a widower, there was no "first lady" to catch the public eye. And to Theodosia fell the feminine honors of the inaugural entertainments. Her youth and beauty, her graceful manners and her wit, became the topics of popular conversation. At the inauguration ceremonies she had the seat of honor, and at the ball that night, in a gown of ivory velvet with white rosebuds in her hair, she led the cotillion on President Jefferson's arm.

When Joseph and Theodosia left for the south, Mr. Burr said good-by to his daughter as calmly as though they were parting for no more than a day or two.

"Mind you see that Theo keeps up her studies," Mr. Burr warned Joseph, as the two men shook hands. "I don't want to find her settled into an empty-headed little housewife next time we meet, interested in nothing but her marketing and a dozen babies."

"I'll make her study harder than ever, sir," Joseph promised. "And I shall send you reports on her progress and misdemeanors."

"And *I* shall fairly dazzle you with my wisdom when you come to visit, Papa." Theodosia laughed. But the next moment she leaned out of the carriage and her glance searched her father's face anxiously. "Papa, you *will* visit us? You promise?"

"Wild horses couldn't keep me from it," Mr. Burr said. And still smiling, he stepped back. Debonair and handsome, he stood with head held high as he waved farewell to the dearest treasure of his life.

# Part Two

·CHARLESTON, 1801–1812·

## ·CHAPTER 12·

# Peacocks on the Lawn

Theodosia's first sight of her new home was through the late dusk of an April afternoon. For nearly three weeks she and Joseph had been traveling over good roads and bad, and on that last afternoon of the journey Theodosia observed with a sigh that she was so heartily tired of being jounced about in a carriage that she meant, when they got home, not to drive anywhere for at least a month.

But when they turned at last into the long avenue that led to the Oaks, her weariness vanished and she leaned out the window to exclaim with delight over the long, low house of pink brick with tall white columns across the front.

"Joseph, it's *beautiful!*" Theodosia's eyes shone. "But it's so very big. Shan't we feel quite lost in it, just the two of us?"

She was leaning out for a second look. The cypress trees that lined the drive were hung with long, misty gray strands of Spanish moss that swung gently in the mild breeze, and in the soft light the lawns on either side looked like wide carpets of velvety green. Suddenly Theodosia clutched at her husband's hand.

"Joseph, there are two *peacocks!*" she exclaimed. "Do they belong to us?"

When he nodded, amused at her childish pleasure, Theodosia settled back beside him with a sigh of purest satisfaction. "Just wait until I write Natalie," she said, "and tell her there are peacocks on the lawn!" As they reached the end of the avenue and drew up before the broad front steps, she quickly smoothed her gloves and set her hat straight. "Do I look all right, Joseph?"

"You look very sweet, my Theo," Joseph said, smiling, "and about ten years old instead of a matronly and settled seventeen."

A few minutes later, when he led her through the door and down the line of household servants who stood in the big front hall to welcome their master and mistress in true plantation style, Joseph watched with pride the air of gentle grace with which his wife took possession of her new home. He saw the faces of the servants break into smiles of welcome as Theodosia paused for a word of greeting to each in turn.

Accustomed as she had always been to the well-staffed household at Richmond Hill, Theodosia nevertheless found herself bewildered at first by the elaborateness of life at the Oaks, and she wrote to Natalie that her greatest difficulty was in remembering just which of the servants to ask for when she wanted some specific task performed.

> Joseph assures me (she wrote) that we have no more servants than any well-regulated plantation—but with so many countenances surrounding me—all looking precisely

alike to my uninitiated eye—I feel like a duchess, and a slightly confused duchess at that! There is a special boy who has no other function in life but to black our boots, another who shines silver night and day, one whose only duty is to carry up vast tubs of hot water and still another who spends all his waking hours (which are not many) in feeding and tending the peacocks who roam on the lawns. And woe be to Theo if I ask the boot-boy to fetch me fresh candles, or the candle-slavy to polish my new riding boots!

As the weeks went by, Theodosia forgot about such small trials in the delights of her new life. The Alstons had a town house in Charleston as well, and Theodosia found Southern society very much to her liking. There were teas and dinners, balls and theaters. The people were gay and friendly, and they seemed quite as charmed with Joseph's bride as she was with them. Indeed, it was no time at all before young Mrs. Alston began to be regarded as the most popular hostess in Charleston.

Theodosia wrote to her father with impatience. He *must* arrange to visit soon. He must see her new home, Joseph's family, and her friends, all of whom, she assured him, were waiting with bated breath for the honor of entertaining the Vice-president.

Mr. Burr replied that he would surely come. Twice he even engaged passage on packet boats sailing for Charleston, but each time there were complications in his plans that made it impossible for him to leave, and he sent, in his stead, long, affectionate letters and parcels containing the most charmingly extravagant gifts for Theodosia and Joseph.

Theodosia was disappointed, but not for long. It was

nearly summer now, and the lovely Southern spring was ending. Instead of mild balmy days, when Joseph and Theodosia rode together or strolled along the embankment in Charleston, the weather turned sultry and oppressive. The wind blew a hot, steady mist from the Carolina swamplands, carrying the threat of fevers and malaria.

Since he could not come to them, Mr. Burr wrote, why should not Theodosia and her husband travel north to join him for the summer months at Richmond Hill?

An excellent plan, said Joseph. And Theodosia agreed.

By the middle of June, the Alstons were traveling once more, and when they reached Richmond Hill, they found Mr. Burr and Natalie already there, and the big house open and ready.

It was the happiest of summers.

Since Congress was not in session, the Vice-president was not required to be in Washington, and Mr. Burr was free to devote himself to the entertainment of his guests. John was with them a good part of the time, and when, in August, Vanderlyn came to Richmond Hill to paint portraits of Natalie and Theodosia, the little group that had been such good companions the summer before was once more united.

Again there were picnics and rides and sailing parties to fill the long bright hours of the summer days and on weekends they often took the big coach and drove far up through the Westchester hills and stopped for the night at some country inn.

Toward the end of August, Mr. Burr left for Washington, and Joseph suggested that he and Theodosia might take a trip across the state that would include a visit to Niagara

Falls. On the return journey, when they had stopped over-
night in Buffalo, their breakfast was interrupted by a startled
servingmaid who informed them that "a naked Indian"
was outside and said he had a letter for Mrs. Alston.

Joseph looked up from his coffee in astonishment. "Upon
my word, Theo," he said. "Have you taken to correspond-
ing with savages?"

He went to see what was wanted, and came back to
report that the Indian was, fortunately, *not* naked, and that
the letter was from Chief Joseph Brant of the Mohawk tribe,
who had often been a guest at Richmond Hill.

Chief Brant had learned that Theodosia was in Buffalo
and wished, he said, to request the honor of a visit from her
and her husband. Would they come and stay at his camp
for a few days, and allow him, in some small measure, to
repay the hospitality that Miss Burr had so kindly offered
to him at her father's house.

They sent the messenger back to say that they would
accept with pleasure, and on the following morning a guide
appeared to lead the way to the Mohawk encampment.
Chief Brant was waiting to receive them, looking more im-
posing than ever, in his native dress, as he bowed low over
Theodosia's hand.

Joseph was pleased at the opportunity of meeting the
famous chief, and the two men spent a great deal of time in
conversation during the next three days, while Theodosia
visited the Indian women in their homes. She watched them
making pottery and grinding the late summer harvest of
corn, and amused the children vastly by allowing them to
investigate the contents of her handbag. The whole settle-

ment seemed charmed by the visitors, and all the tribe, from the tallest and fiercest-looking elder to the smallest toddling infant, showed the guests every possible courtesy.

When the Alstons were ready to leave, the camp gathered around to see them off, and nearly every one insisted on presenting the "Graceful One" and the "Handsome One" with a parting gift.

The Alstons stopped for a few days at Richmond Hill before beginning the long journey home to Charleston. Although Mr. Burr was able to join them there, and they had a last pleasant visit together, the easy, carefree spell of summer seemed to have vanished. There was frost in the September nights that touched the Palisades with red and gold, and a haze of autumn hung over the last stray blooms that lingered in the gardens.

Natalie was planning a trip to France to visit her mother, and since Mr. Burr was to be in Washington for the winter, it had been decided that Richmond Hill was to be closed.

On the last day before her departure, Theodosia wandered from room to room in the big house. The furniture, shrouded in dust covers, already had a forlorn and deserted look.

"Oh, dear," Theo sighed, "I do *wish* you weren't going to France, Natalie. It makes me feel homesick already to think of Richmond Hill being left alone and empty."

"I know." Natalie nodded soberly. "I'm afraid I shall be most desperately homesick myself. We've been so happy here." She broke off suddenly, as a shadow of a frown crossed

Theodosia's face. "Theo, you aren't worrying about Papa for any reason, are you?"

Theodosia said slowly, "I don't know. He seems very well, I think, though he works too hard, and is tired sometimes. But that's not what troubles me, Natalie. It's the things people keep saying about him. That he's too ambitious—and all the long trouble with Mr. Hamilton."

"Ah, yes, Mr. Hamilton." Natalie sighed. "If only that dreadful business with Hamilton had never started. It's silly for grown men to act so! Hamilton determined to make Papa angry—and Papa equally determined not to *be* angry. Sometimes"—she whisked a handful of silver out of the chest she was packing and rattled it briskly—"I feel like *shaking* the two of them!"

Theodosia smiled at that, but after a moment she went on soberly, "Of course I'd never dare speak to Papa about any of it. He'd be furious, I know, for he'll never admit that the slightest thing is wrong. But sometimes I wonder if he doesn't try to carry too much alone. Joseph says he doesn't believe any man can keep the self-control Papa does forever. He says he's afraid someday it might break, and then" —Theodosia spread her hands—"I don't know what might happen."

John and Vanderlyn had already gone, and Joseph had driven into the city. Mr. Burr and the two girls had their supper in front of the study hearth that evening, since the dining-room things were packed away. Peggy sent up platters of cold turkey, bread and pickles and cheese, and a big pot of hot, rich chocolate. Sitting before the fire, they were very cozy and contented. It was like old times, Natalie said. Yet it wasn't quite like old times, for Natalie's thoughts were already of her journey to France, and Theodosia kept listening for Joseph's carriage and jumping up to look out the window each time she thought she heard it.

Only Mr. Burr was the same. He was in excellent spirits, and as he talked on about his life in Washington, amusing them with stories about the people he had met there, Theodosia watched his face, dark and handsome in the firelight, and wondered whether perhaps her fears and doubts were foolish, after all.

They had nearly finished supper when the door opened suddenly and Joseph came into the room. He still wore his cloak, and in one hand he carried a folded newspaper, which he handed at once to Mr. Burr.

"I'm sorry to burst in like this, sir," Joseph said, "but I think you ought to see this right away." He pointed to an article on the front page. "It's a new attack on you, and a thoroughly contemptible one."

Joseph's face was grave as he waited for Mr. Burr to comment.

But, having glanced through the article, Mr. Burr merely laid aside the paper without comment.

"What is it, Papa?" Theodosia reached for the paper.

Mr. Burr shrugged. "Nothing much," he said. "Only some anonymous writer airing his views about the Vice-president."

"But this is different, sir." Joseph set his chin stubbornly. "This writer claims that you are actually plotting to overthrow Jefferson and take the presidency for yourself. Even though the whole thing is a preposterous lie, it's causing a tremendous stir, I assure you. The whole city is talking about nothing else. It's bound to get back to Mr. Jefferson, and unless you deny the charges and give proof, there are certain people, even in your own party, who will believe these things."

"Will they?" Mr. Burr asked calmly. He poured a cup of chocolate and handed it to Joseph with a smile.

Joseph shook his head impatiently. "I'm aware, of course," he said, "that you expect to have enemies. So does any man in public life. But I think you're going too far when you allow these vicious and unfounded lies to go undefended."

"You forget one thing, Joseph." Mr. Burr leaned back in his chair. "To defend oneself is to admit that there is a charge worth denying. To defend oneself against an enemy is meaningless. Against my friend Hamilton"—he paused, with a shrug—"it's hopeless."

A silence followed his words.

Theodosia glanced at her husband's face. She had seldom seen Joseph as near to anger as he was now. In her heart she believed Joseph was right, and she longed to say so—to beg her father, just this once, to take Joseph's advice and defend himself against Mr. Hamilton's attacks. She might have spoken, but a warning flashed to her from the bland, impassive depths of her father's eyes and she felt the words die in her throat.

"Trust me, Theodosia," his look seemed to say. "Trust me—believe only in me."

She looked down, still silent.

"Come, Joseph." Mr. Burr stood up. "We've upset Theo by all this talk. We'll say no more about it. As for this"—he picked up the newspaper and walked to the fireplace—"we can dispose of it quite easily." He tossed the crumpled pages into the flames.

"How shall we amuse ourselves this last evening?" Mr. Burr asked. "A game of cards?" He walked over to put his hand affectionately on the young man's shoulder. "I know you mean well, Joseph, but please believe me, I know best how to deal with these things."

"It's for you to decide, of course, sir." Joseph nodded.

Theodosia was relieved to see that the anger had died out of Joseph's blue eyes. And as she and Natalie rose to fetch the cards, she passed the fireplace and noticed that the last fragments of paper had vanished, leaving only a bed of coals that burned bright and steady on the hearth.

## CHAPTER 13

# Little Gampy

I T WAS MID-OCTOBER when the Alstons reached South Carolina again, and Theodosia was soon caught up once more in the affairs of her two households and the pleasant round of social events.

But, although she and Joseph continued to entertain and be entertained, Theodosia was not content to become entirely absorbed by the round of teas and dinners. The habit of studying, instilled by years of training, was not easily forgotten, and she still reported faithfully to her father. From him she received encouragement and suggestions. Once, being pleased by a pretty turn of phrase in one of her letters, he observed: ". . . Your letters contain now and then a spark of Promethean fire: a spark, mind ye; don't be vain." Another time he advised that it would be "better to lose your head than your habits of study."

The example of Theodosia's industry made its mark on Joseph. Encouraged by her, and by occasional advice from Mr. Burr, Joseph began to take his plans for a career in politics more seriously. He ran for the state legislature and was elected. Before long his keen judgment and enthusiastic interest in public affairs established him as one of the rising young statesmen of the South.

Theodosia was delighted by her husband's success, and as she became more and more engrossed by his career and the pleasant diversions of her own life, the old days at Richmond Hill faded gradually into the background. There was no time to think on the past; no place in her full, happy days for homesickness.

Natalie, too, seemed to have been caught up in such a whirl of new experiences that she had no regrets for the old days she had left behind. Her letters to Theodosia were filled with accounts of good times and pleasant friends in Paris, and in particular of a certain Mr. Thomas Sumpter whom she had met.

"Our Natalie is in love," Theodosia observed at breakfast one morning. "And a very good thing too. Papa says Mr. Sumpter will be a splendid husband for her."

"Upon my word, what a pair of matchmakers you and your papa are." Joseph laughed. "You have Natalie's future all settled between you before she's so much as breathed a word about it herself. Can this be the same Theo who used to argue with me over the folly of any woman marrying before she was in her dotage? How you have changed, my dear."

Theodosia buttered a toasted scone and nibbled at the corner of it thoughtfully. "If you weren't such an utterly misguided male, Mr. Alston," she said, "you might take my attitude as a very pretty compliment for yourself. But since

I must be plain about it, I'll confess that having tried married life and found it *very much* to my liking, I'm naturally anxious for everyone else to enter into the same state of bliss. As for Natalie—just wait, and you'll see that I was right."

Surely enough, a few days after the bells of St. Michael's Church had rung the New Year into Charleston, a letter came from Paris saying that Natalie was engaged and would soon be married. "My mother thoroughly approves of the match and is charmed with Mr. Sumpter, whom," she added ingenuously, "you may recall my having spoken of once or twice before. As for myself, I am deliriously happy, a state that none can understand more completely than you, dear Theo."

"So you see, Joseph," Theodosia said, "I *was* right."

And Joseph was content merely to shake his head wonderingly and kiss the tip of his wife's pretty nose.

In the late spring of that year, it was at last arranged for Mr. Burr to visit Charleston. The Congress having adjourned early, he was able to leave Washington on the first of May, and wrote that he was "proceeding south with the speed of lightning."

For days in advance Theodosia was busy preparing for her father's arrival, and her friends were so anxious to show the Vice-president every hospitality that dinners, dances, luncheons, and even breakfast parties were arranged in his honor. Joseph must bring him to a hunt breakfast—and, of course, without fail, he must go to St. Michael's on Sunday morning and sit in the celebrities' pew where General Washington had sat.

Mr. Burr was charmed by everything. He made himself such an agreeable and entertaining guest that, by the end of his stay, someone observed that "half of Charleston is entirely infatuated with the Vice-president, and the other half is furious over not having had the chance to entertain him!"

The real event of his visit, however, did not take place until the end of June. That was the birth of a little son to Joseph and Theodosia.

Never was a baby more enthusiastically welcomed. Mr. Burr, quite as much as the young parents, threw himself into preparations for the event with a frenzy of plans, anticipations, and general to-do.

For days in advance everything was in readiness at the Oaks. Mr. Burr had commissioned Natalie to buy the most beautiful cradle obtainable in Paris. Joseph's mother had sent the faithful Mammy who had cared for her own children when they were babies. The doctor in attendance was personally instructed, by the Vice-president, as to his solemn responsibility in ushering the new Alston into existence. Every detail of Theodosia's welfare and health was supervised with such scrupulous care by her husband and father that she declared at last that she felt as if the future of the whole human race might well depend on her ability to produce a satisfactory infant.

On the twenty-ninth of June, Aaron Burr Alston was born.

He was a healthy, handsome, entirely charming baby, and he so delighted his father and grandfather that by the time Theodosia was up and about again, she complained, with some justice, that it was no longer possible to have a conversation with Joseph or her father that did not center on the perfections of her remarkable son.

"A finely shaped head," Mr. Burr declared solemnly. "See how rounded his brow is, a sure sign of intellect and good judgment."

"He has his mother's eyes, don't you think?" Joseph put in. "And obviously a good wit, too. This morning he smiled very plainly when I showed him a new rattle. Mammy says he shows far more sense than any of us did at the same age."

Mammy said much else besides. She complained bitterly to Theodosia that it was quite impossible to bring up a baby properly with two great men constantly underfoot, cluttering up the nursery with enough toys for fifty babies, and hanging over her honey lamb at all hours.

Mr. Burr stayed at the Oaks until the middle of July, unwilling to tear himself away from the fascinating spectacle of his grandson. When it at last became apparent that the Vice-president had obligations besides being the most devoted and attentive grandpapa ever seen, he left for Washington. But it was arranged before his departure that as soon as Theodosia and the baby were able, Joseph would bring them for a visit to New York, where Mr. Burr promised to open Richmond Hill especially for them.

By Christmas the three Alstons were back in Charleston, and from that time on the letters from Theodosia to her father were filled with accounts of the behavior and accomplishments of little Aaron. As soon as he could talk, she taught him to say "Grandpa," which he twisted into *Gampy,* and for a while that became the baby's own nickname.

In every letter Mr. Burr demanded "more of Gampy's doings." Before the boy had passed his first birthday, Mr. Burr had already laid out elaborate plans for his training and education, and meanwhile he delighted in sending most extravagant gifts to the whole family. Little suits of embroidered linen, patent-leather boots, and dozens of toys for Gampy. The latest bonnets, gloves from Paris, laces, scent, and furs for Theodosia; and for Joseph, books from England and France. When Theodosia wrote that they were remodeling the big pink-brick plantation house, Mr. Burr immediately commissioned Natalie to buy a whole suite of French furniture for Theodosia's sitting room. And once, when Theo complained of the scarcity of good cooks in the South, Mr. Burr lost no time in locating one in New York and dispatching her to Charleston on the next packet, with his compliments.

In the spring of 1803, Theodosia fell ill with malaria. For nearly four weeks the fever raged, and in spite of all the medical advice and care that her distracted husband could summon, her recovery was slow and difficult. She was depressed and miserable. She worried about herself, about her husband, and her boy. Most of all she was troubled about her father. The old fears, never quite forgotten, came back to plague her restless nights and weary days, until at last Mr. Burr became alarmed by the gloomy cast of her letters and insisted that Joseph leave his work as soon as possible and bring her north.

Joseph was only too glad to do anything that might bring back his wife's health and high spirits, and on the eve of

Theodosia's birthday, they arrived in New York by boat and were driven straight to Richmond Hill.

But not even the welcome that awaited her there, nor all the loving care and attention her husband and father gave her throughout the quiet summer, seemed quite to restore Theodosia. When autumn came, and she was still pale and languid, Mr. Burr talked long and earnestly with Joseph.

It was plain to be seen, he said, that the Southern climate had not agreed with Theodosia. Why not stay in New York, instead of taking her back to the danger of more fevers from the swamplands of Carolina? Joseph could take up politics in New York, quite as well as in the South. Mr. Burr would see to it that he met the right people, made the proper connections. . . .

But Joseph, for all his unbounded devotion to Theodosia, could be firm. He would *not,* he said, trade on his father-in-law's prominence. He had begun his career by his own efforts in the South, and there he would continue it. Charleston was his home, and Theodosia's home and, for better or for worse, they would return to Charleston.

And return they did.

If Theodosia regretted her husband's decision, she was too much her father's daughter ever to show her disappointment, and at every stopping place on the return journey she sent back little notes to her father designed to reassure him of her health and good spirits.

The Alstons stopped a few days in Washington, and from there Theodosia sent Mr. Burr a long letter telling of the people they had seen. Dolley Madison had come to call at once, and had been charmed with little Gampy. They were entertained by various of Mr. Burr's friends in the capital, but, strangely, no invitation came to them from the President.

Mr. Jefferson could scarcely have failed to know that the Vice-president's daughter was in Washington, yet he sent no word of greeting. And although Theodosia made no comment to her father on the omission, she was more than ever disturbed by the persistent rumors of the ill feeling between the President and Mr. Burr.

On the last morning of their stay, a chambermaid brought the morning tray, and being disposed to gossip, she lingered while Theodosia had her breakfast.

"We don't like seeing you go, ma'am, and that's the truth," the girl said. "It's all about town that Mr. Burr is a gentleman not to be trusted—and folks here were near ready to believe it until you came with Mr. Alston and the little boy. But it doesn't appear likely, as I was saying myself this morning in the kitchen, that any gentleman connected with *you,* ma'am, could be the sort of rapscallion they talk of Mr. Burr's being. That it doesn't."

Theodosia put down her cup slowly. Ordinarily she would have been impatient of such gossip, but now she wondered.

"What sort of things do they say of my father?" she asked.

"Oh"—the girl folded her arms under her apron—"it's more a question of what *don't* they say, ma'am. The tales we hear about the plots and deviltries our Vice-president is up to. Some say he's trying to be President himself."

Theodosia glanced up quickly, and a little shiver of

fear went through her as she saw the girl's eyes, pale and credulous, fastened eagerly on hers. Then, remembering herself, she forced a smile.

"I don't think those things are true," Theodosia said quietly. "I really don't."

"Nor do I, ma'am." The girl shook her head. "But all the same it's a pity more people who talk so against Mr. Burr can't know *you,* ma'am. They'd stop then." She nodded her head with decision. "I know they would!"

Over and over, on the long journey home, Theodosia kept hearing again the singsong voice of the chambermaid. Leaning back in the carriage, her eyes closed against the dull ache of fatigue that pounded in her head with every jolt over the dusty, rutted roads, she kept wondering whether perhaps the girl had been right.

Would it really make a difference if she were with her father more? If, instead of being so much alone, he had the stabilizing influence of a family—of herself, and Joseph, and little Aaron? Was it true that Mr. Jefferson no longer trusted her father, that even his friends were beginning to suspect him of plots and schemes?

The questions circled in her mind until they seemed to mingle with the rumble of the wheels and the monotonous swaying of the carriage, and Theodosia pressed her hands against her ears as if to shut them out forever. Then, suddenly, she seemed to hear her father speak, as he had long ago when she was a child and frightened of something. "Courage," she seemed to hear him whisper. "Courage, Theodosia."

## ·CHAPTER 14·

# The Gathering Clouds

ON A BRIGHT summer's morning Theodosia and Natalie sat side by side on the veranda steps of the Alstons' summer cabin in the Carolina mountains. A fortnight past, Natalie and her husband and their little daughter had landed in New York from abroad. There Mr. Sumpter learned that he would be required to make a business trip to Charleston, so he had brought his family south with him, and while he stayed in the city to complete his work, Natalie and her little girl visited Theodosia.

The mountain air was crystal clear and pleasantly cool, and a light breeze whispered through the tall pines now and then, gently ruffling the curls of the two children who played together near the steps.

For the first few days of the visit, Theodosia and Natalie had talked almost without stopping. There had been so much to tell, so many questions to be asked and answered, after their long separation. Now, sitting together in the peaceful silence of the morning sunshine, they watched the children.

"How well they play together, don't they, Theo?" Natalie asked presently, smiling to see how her fair-haired little girl, named for Theodosia, insisted on giving her favorite doll to Gampy.

Theodosia nodded. "I'm afraid your young Theo will spoil my young Aaron, though," she said. "She gives him all her best toys, and last night at supper she refused to eat a bite until she had fed Gampy all the nicest bits of chicken from her plate. Joseph says it's plainly a case of love at first sight."

"Oh, it's *so* good to be here, Theo," Natalie said. "I used to wonder sometimes, when we were in France, whether we'd ever really be together again. And now to have this lovely visit, and to find you and Joseph so well . . ." She smiled. "You know, Theo, I had no idea what a success Joseph was making. They even talk of his running for governor of the state."

"I know." There was pride in Theodosia's voice. "He deserves to succeed, Natalie, he's worked so hard and faithfully." She paused. "Natalie, Papa *was* all right when you saw him in New York, wasn't he? You've told me so little about him."

Natalie did not reply at once. Leaning down, she scooped up a handful of pine needles, and let them trickle slowly through her fingers. "There wasn't much to tell," she said guardedly. "He seemed in good spirits. But . . ."

"But what, Natalie?"

Natalie tossed away the pine needles and brushed the soft dust from her fingers, frowning a little.

"I know I oughtn't to trouble you, Theo, but all the while Thomas and I were in New York, we kept hearing the most fantastic rumors. It seemed as if, wherever we went, people talked of nothing but *Burr—Burr—Burr.* All the old stories, you know"—she paused and sighed—"about his debts, and the fact that he and Mr. Jefferson had quarreled, and that Jefferson accuses him of trying to split the party and turn his friends against the President. It seems that Mr. Hamilton has been more bitter than ever against Papa. I don't understand it very well, Theo, but I'll admit that the stories troubled me, though Papa himself only laughed when Thomas tried to talk to him. He said that the rumors were nothing more than fancies spread by Hamilton and Clinton and the other Federalists. I wonder sometimes, Theo, whether so much bitterness and distrust hasn't changed Papa, and made *him* bitter and distrustful of others, I mean, even though he'll never admit it."

"I know," Theodosia answered soberly. She bent down to smooth her little son's dark head as he climbed up the step to lay a pine cone in her lap. "Oh, Natalie, if only that old quarrel with Mr. Hamilton could die. I've so hoped and prayed it might."

Natalie shook her head. "There's one comfort at least, Theo. The old quarrel has gone on for so many years that it's hardly likely now that anything will ever come of it. And whatever happens, Theo—whatever people may say against Papa—I'll always trust him."

"So shall I," Theodosia said. "As long as I live."

That was the morning of June 17 , 1804.

In the afternoon of that same day, William Van Ness presented himself at the town house of Mr. Hamilton in New York.

He delivered a letter to Hamilton from Aaron Burr, and a copy of a newspaper with two sentences underlined. One said that Mr. Hamilton considered Burr a dangerous man, not to be trusted with the reins of government. The other that there was "a still more despicable opinion which General Hamilton has expressed of Mr. Burr."

In the letter which Van Ness carried, Mr. Burr called Hamilton's attention to the marked passages, and demanded "a prompt and unqualified acknowledgment or denial."

Mr. Hamilton was astonished. He had not, he said, seen the statements until this moment. He must have time to consider them, and Mr. Burr's note, before he could give an answer.

When, after two days, he did reply, it was to state at length that he could make neither the acknowledgment nor the denial that Burr had demanded. He could not consent to be questioned as to the justice of the *inferences* of things he had said of an opponent during fifteen years' competition. He trusted that Colonel Burr, upon further reflection, would see the matter in the same light. If not, he could only regret the fact, and accept the consequences.

During the next few days, several more letters were exchanged, and it became clear that the long battle between the two men had at last reached a climax. Neither would yield an inch. There was only one means left to settle the matter.

Burr challenged Hamilton to a duel, and Hamilton accepted the challenge.

On the twenty-third of June, Van Ness and Mr. Hamilton's second, Mr. Pendleton, met to decide the final details. The duel would take place on July eleventh, at seven in the morning: the place, Weehawken; the weapons, pistols; the distance, ten full paces.

That was all.

The twenty-third of June chanced also to be Theodosia's twenty-first birthday, and in the evening Mr. Burr entertained some friends for dinner at Richmond Hill. Writing to Theodosia the next morning, he said nothing of the coming duel, but he was careful to tell her about the party the evening before. They had, Mr. Burr said, "laughed an hour, and danced an hour, and drunk her health." He had brought her picture to the dinner table and put it in the place where she usually sat.

In the last days before the duel, both Mr. Burr and Mr. Hamilton went about their businesses quite as usual. No one except themselves and their seconds knew what was to take place.

Under the code of the times, Hamilton had had no choice but to accept Burr's challenge. Dueling was still the accepted custom in settling disputes between gentlemen, and there were few men in public life who had not taken part in a duel for one reason or another. Both Burr and Hamilton had fought before. Three years earlier Mr. Hamilton's son Philip had been shot and killed on the dueling field. That two men who had been such long and bitter enemies should fight was in no way surprising. The only surprising part was that Burr, who had borne in stubborn silence so many injuries and insults from Mr. Hamilton, should now suddenly, without warning, demand the ultimate revenge for a comparatively mild and insignificant slur.

What moved Burr to break his years of stoical silence, no one was ever to know. For in this moment as in all others, Mr. Burr kept his own counsel.

## ·CHAPTER 15·

# The Distance: Ten Full Paces

THE NIGHT BEFORE the duel Mr. Burr dined alone at Richmond Hill. Later he went to his study, and there he sat before his desk for a long while, writing, arranging his affairs with methodical care. At last the desk was clear of papers, and everything was done. All was finished, except for one last thing. To write two letters.

Mr. Burr drew a fresh sheet of paper, and paused for a moment staring at the blank white square. Then he dipped his pen, and began to write:

"My dear Joseph . . ."

It was very still in the room. Outside the open windows the summer night lay dark. Now and then a faint breeze sent the candle flames flickering. Only the far-off sound of the crickets' chirping and the steady scratching of the pen broke the silence, as Mr. Burr wrote:

> . . . If it should be my lot to fall, yet I shall live in you and Theodosia and your son. I commit to you all that is most dear to me—my reputation and my daughter. . . .

Let me entreat you to stimulate and aid Theodosia in
the cultivation of her mind. It is indispensable to her
happiness, and essential to yours. . . . She will richly com-
pensate your trouble. . . .

The letter done, and sealed, Mr. Burr laid it aside and
bent once more over the desk.

"My dearest Theodosia . . ."

This was a longer letter. It held no bitterness, no regrets,
no explanation of what was to take place on the morrow.
Only calm, dispassionate directions for the disposition of his
affairs. To Theodosia he committed all his belongings, his
letters, and what property might remain when his estate
was settled.

. . . Tell my dear Natalie that I have not left her anything, for the very good reason that I had nothing to leave
to anyone. My estate will just about pay my debts and no
more. . . . Give her one of the pictures of me. There
are three in this house; one by Stuart, and two by Vanderlyn. . . .

John and Frederic were to have his clothes, a seal of
General Washington was to be saved for Gampy, and he
begged Theodosia to see that the faithful servants at Richmond Hill were provided for, and, if possible, kept on in the
Alstons' service.

That was all, but for a last few lines:

. . . I am indebted to you, my dearest Theodosia, for a
very great portion of the happiness which I have enjoyed
in this life. You have completely satisfied all that my
heart and affections had hoped or even wished. With a
little more perseverance, determination, and industry, you
will obtain all that ambition or vanity had fondly imag-

ined. Let your son have occasion to be proud that he had a mother. Adieu. Adieu.

A. Burr

It was scarcely daybreak when Van Ness came into the room and wakened Mr. Burr. Everything was ready, he said. The boat was waiting at the river landing. As they walked together down the path to the water's edge, a fresh breeze blew from the west and light, fluffy clouds scudded across the sky. Mr. Burr climbed quickly into the boat, and sat in the stern, his eye fixed on the line of the Jersey shore while Van Ness rowed steadily across the river and tied the boat to the trunk of a young tree by the shallow water.

In silence the two men made their way up from the shore to a place where they emerged into a flat, open clearing. There they laid aside their coats, and while Van Ness got out the pistols and examined them, Mr. Burr stood looking through the trees toward the broad river that sparkled and glittered in the morning sun.

"It's a quarter to seven, Mr. Burr," Van Ness said. "Are you ready?"

Aaron Burr nodded.

There was a sound of footsteps. Three men came into the clearing. Mr. Hamilton, his fine face as composed as Burr's; Mr. Pendleton; and Dr. Hosack, a physician.

The principals and seconds exchanged the customary word of greeting. Then, saying no more, they made their final preparations. Ten full paces were measured; the two men took their places.

When Pendleton handed Mr. Hamilton his pistol, he asked if he should set the hairspring.

Without turning his head, Mr. Hamilton said in a quiet voice, "Not this time, Pendleton."

The seconds withdrew, the men stood waiting.

"Are you ready?"

Both nodded.

Van Ness spoke the word. "Present."

Each raised his arm, and Burr took quiet, deliberate aim and fired.

Somewhere above Mr. Hamilton's head a bird had been singing, a sweet cadence of notes that fell upon the sunlit air. As the sound of the shot shattered the stillness of the woods, the bird's song ceased and there was a startled whir of wings as it sprang up and away from the low bough.

Silence for a split second—then another shot. Hamilton's finger had closed on the trigger and in the instant before he crumpled to the ground, his wild shot struck a branch high above Burr's head.

Pendleton and the doctor sprang forward to where General Hamilton lay motionless. Burr moved toward him also, but before he had taken more than a step, Van Ness was at his side, urging him to come down to the boat at once.

On the trip back, Mr. Burr sat again in the stern. Everything in the calm scene was as before. The two men were as silent, the sky as blue, the clouds as white, and the broad waters of the Hudson still flashing clear beneath the morning sun—all was as before—except that somewhere, hidden among the trees on the receding shore, a man lay mortally wounded.

And a bird, his song cut short, had flown away.

·CHAPTER 16·

# *"Hang Burr!"*

B Y MIDMORNING THE streets of lower New York were
milling with people. They came out of shops and of-
fices, up from the docks and out of their homes, shocked by
the news that spread through the city like wildfire.

At the house to which General Hamilton had been carried, a crowd gathered, silent and tense, waiting for the
bulletins that came each hour. Mrs. Hamilton, with her children, had hurried into the room where, behind drawn shutters, her husband lay dying.

Handbills, hastily printed, appeared on the street corners.
Everywhere, on every tongue, the news was discussed with
indignation and horror.

"Burr has murdered Hamilton!"

"Burr has escaped . . ."

"It was a fair duel, fairly fought . . ."

"Burr provoked it . . ."

"No, Hamilton provoked it . . ."

"They say Burr has disappeared . . ."

"Pendleton swears that Hamilton intended deliberately to fire into the air. He says Hamilton refused to have the hairspring set for his first shot."

"If Hamilton dies, this will ruin Burr, no matter who was to blame."

Through the crowds, from lip to lip, the rumors flew—confused and contradictory. But always they came back to the same verdict. The Vice-president had *murdered* General Hamilton, and in the swelling tide of public anger and grief, it was forgotten that the two men had met under fair and honorable conditions, according to the accepted rules of dueling.

Shortly after noon, a young man rode up Broadway and stopped his horse at the corner of Wall Street, to dismount in the midst of a group gathered by the steps of Trinity Church. Puzzled by the crowds and excitement, he inquired of a passer-by what had happened.

The stranger stared at him curiously.

"You haven't heard? Why, the Vice-president met General Hamilton in a duel this morning, and Hamilton was wounded and is dying. They say Burr has already escaped. He's disappeared, they say, and——"

An expression of blankest astonishment and disbelief came over the young man's face as he shook his head. "There must be some mistake. I've just come from breakfast with Colonel Burr. He is my uncle. He said nothing of a duel." Still bewildered, the young man turned to where the poster blazoned the news in bold, unmistakable letters. Then, without another word, or a glance for the crowd that still muttered angrily around him, he mounted and wheeled his horse back toward the Greenwich Road.

Mr. Burr was in his study when the young man rushed in breathlessly. Seated at his desk, he was engaged in writing a letter, but when he looked up to see his nephew's distraught countenance, Mr. Burr laid down his pen with an air of courteous surprise. "What brings you back so soon, Edward?" he asked. "Has something happened?"

For a full moment the young man stood speechless. Then, flinging himself into a chair, he launched into an account of what was happening in the streets of the city. The angry crowds—the rumors—the printed bulletins crying the news of the duel from every corner.

Mr. Burr listened calmly. "All this is very surprising," he said. "It is true that I met General Hamilton in a duel this morning. It's also true that it was I who challenged. But everyone knows that I had far more than ample grounds for challenging. For fifteen years Hamilton has provoked me, insulted me, libeled my name, and deliberately attempted to ruin me at every turn. A dozen times before I might have challenged him. Indeed, I've been advised to do so more than once. And we met fairly. General Hamilton had precisely the same chance as I this morning——"

"I know, Uncle. But, I tell you, no one is considering that now. They say you killed him deliberately. There's even talk of hanging you for *murder*. If Hamilton dies, they say——" He stopped short, startled by a move from Mr. Burr.

*"They say,"* Mr. Burr repeated, in a voice of bitterest

scorn. Leaning forward across the desk, he faced his nephew with blazing anger in his dark eyes. "Be kind enough not to speak those odious words to me again. Do you think I care a rap for what *they say?*" With a gesture of rare violence, he brought his hand down sharply on the polished mahogany desk. "Name me a critic, and I'll answer him. Name me a hundred, I'll answer them all—gladly. But I cannot, and will not, listen to what *they say.*"

"I'm sorry, Uncle, truly." The young man drew back. "I only meant to warn you—to ask what you are planning to do now?"

Mr. Burr sat back in his chair and, as if all emotion had been erased from his features with a sponge, he eyed his nephew with his usual impassive composure.

"Do?" Mr. Burr inquired calmly. "I don't propose to do anything."

"But, Uncle, surely, in view of the general feeling, it would be better if you were to go away for at least a few days, until things have settled down."

"I scarcely think," Mr. Burr said quietly, "that it would do my cause any good to run away. No man has even been hanged for taking part in a fair duel. Believe me, Edward, the choice was not mine. It was Hamilton who chose to make me his enemy—not I him."

The young man rose.

"Just as you say, sir, of course. But if they should carry out their threat of indicting you for murder . . ."

"Then," said Mr. Burr, "they will at least be spared the trouble of having to hunt me out. If I'm wanted, I shall be right here—waiting."

"And is there anything you want me to do in the meanwhile, sir?"

Mr. Burr glanced up kindly.

"You might stay for luncheon with me, if you will."

It was an afternoon ten days later when Theodosia heard the news of the duel. She and Natalie had driven down from the mountains to do some shopping in Charleston. The bundles were being piled into the back of their carriage when Theodosia remembered a certain small stuffed kitty she had intended to buy and take back to Gampy.

"Wait for me here," she called to Natalie. "There's one thing more that I'd forgotten."

A few minutes passed, while Natalie sat in the carriage, idly watching the people who came and went along the embankment on the water front. A packet boat was just in the harbor from New York.

Suddenly her eye was caught by the figure of a young man standing near the dock. There was something familiar about the set of his shoulders and the way he held his tall beaver hat tucked under one arm. He turned just then, and with a cry of surprise, Natalie was out of the carriage and running toward him.

"Mr. Vanderlyn," she called, nearly tripping over her full muslin skirts in her eagerness. "Mr. Vanderlyn. . . ."

He turned quickly, and for a moment his sober face lighted. "Oh, Miss Natalie, it's good to see you." He took her hand in his.

"But this is wonderful. We hadn't a notion that you were in Charleston, Mr. Vanderlyn. Did you just get here?

Theodosia will be delighted, I know. She'll be along in just a minute."

"Miss Natalie, wait." He held fast to her hand as she drew him toward the carriage. "I must speak to you first. There's bad news, I'm afraid. Mr. Burr sent me down by the first boat because he feared that otherwise Theodosia might be alarmed by the rumors that are being spread about him. . . ."

As briefly as possible, Vanderlyn told her what had happened. Of General Hamilton's death on the day following the duel, and of the unexpected and wholly unprecedented tide of public fury that had been roused against Mr. Burr. A fury that had reached its culmination on the afternoon of the funeral, when Mrs. Hamilton and her children had stood beside the coffin on the steps of Trinity Church, and the whole city had gone into mourning. All day the boats in the harbor had boomed their solemn salute of guns, and from every steeple the bells tolled through the melancholy streets below.

"There's never been anything like it, Miss Natalie," Vanderlyn said, his face strained and grave. "General Hamilton was a popular man—even a great man—but I think no one could have foreseen the way his death affected people. They could talk of nothing else, think of nothing else, and everything that had led up to the duel was forgotten. There wasn't any thought of justice or fair play in anyone's mind, only loyalty to the fallen hero and a hatred against the man who had the ironic good fortune to escape from the duel alive."

Natalie shook her head slowly. "I can't believe it," she said in a stunned voice. "I can't believe that Papa—after all

those years when he'd never say one word to defend himself against Mr. Hamilton—would suddenly change like
that." She turned quickly. "Oh, what ever made him do it,
Mr. Vanderlyn?"

"No one knows," he said. "Mr. Burr says nothing—only
that what is done is done. Even now he won't defend his action, no matter how his friends try to persuade him. I think
he must have been as surprised as anyone by the people's attitude, yet he won't admit it. You know how he can be—
stubborn as iron, on the surface, and never letting you see for
an instant what he's really feeling——" He stopped short, as
he looked up to see Theodosia coming out of the shop door.

She walked quickly toward the carriage, the stuffed kitty
in one hand, and in the other a long-legged rag doll she
had found for Natalie's little girl. Her face was shaded pret-
tily by a broad-brimmed leghorn hat. Catching sight of Vanderlyn, Theodosia's eyes lighted with pleasure, but her gay
greeting died on her lips as she saw his grave expression and
Natalie's white face.

"Mr. Vanderlyn, has something happened to my father?" Theodosia asked.

As gently as possible, he told her. When he had finished,
she was silent for a moment. Then, with a queer, choked cry,
she covered her face with her hands.

"Oh, poor Mrs. Hamilton," she said. "What a terrible
thing for her."

Theodosia's slender body swayed, but as Vanderlyn and
Natalie moved to steady her, she straightened quickly and
looked up, her eyes clear and strangely calm.

"And my father?" she asked quietly. "Where is he, Mr. Vanderlyn?"

Her father was quite safe, Vanderlyn assured her. He explained how Mr. Burr had insisted on remaining at Richmond Hill, stubbornly refusing to listen to the counsel of his friends who advised him to leave. His only concern, Vanderlyn said, was the fear that Theodosia would be alarmed by the wild rumors that were being published and circulated.

"He asked me to come straight to you, Miss Theodosia, and to say that he is well, and quite safe. As soon as he is able, he'll let you know his immediate plans, and in the meantime, he said I was to give you one special message."

"What was it, Mr. Vanderlyn?"

"He said, 'Tell Theodosia to remember just one word—*courage.*'"

In the days that followed, lengthening miserably into weeks, Theodosia had more than one occasion to summon her father's message to her mind. The news came that her father had been indicted for murder by the state of New Jersey. Then came a burst of rumors and speculation: that Mr. Burr had escaped, and was in hiding; that there had been attempts to assassinate him; that he was threatened with impeachment; that President Jefferson had refused to intercede in Burr's defense.

Through it all Theodosia waited for some word from her father. And while she waited she wrote to him—long letters in which she told him the news of herself, and Joseph's work, and little Gampy. Cheerful letters, and never a word of reproach for what he had done. Never a single question, nor a hint of what she was suffering in the long nights when she lay awake, listening to the wind in the pines, and haunted always by the memory of Mrs. Hamilton with her sweetly gentle ways.

Whether her letters were reaching their destination, Theodosia could not know. But at last, on an afternoon in August when the mountain air was filled with a mellow, golden haze, Joseph drove up from Charleston and went directly to Theodosia's sitting room to hand her a letter.

In silence she read the few lines—undated, brief. They explained nothing, told her only that her father had left Richmond Hill, and that he was well.

> . . . I shall journey somewhere within a few days, but whither is not yet decided. My heart will travel southward, and repose on the hills of Carolina. Adieu, my dear child . . .

A few days later came another letter, this time dated from Philadelphia. Two of Theodosia's letters had been forwarded to him, and he was pleased to find in one of them an account of some little incident involving Gampy. Still there was no word of his plans, no hint of remorse or regret for what had happened, except for one passage near the end. "Don't let me have the idea that you are dissatisfied with me for a moment," Aaron Burr had written. "I can't just now endure it."

That was all.

Shortly before the time when the Alstons were to leave the mountains, more news came. Mr. Burr wrote that he expected to travel for a while before the opening of Congress made it necessary for him to return to Washington. There was no cause for alarm. The indictment for murder, still pending against him, had been a mere gesture, an expression of hysterical protest, and the action would doubtless come to nothing and be forgotten. For the present it was considered advisable for Mr. Burr to drop out of the public eye, and he proposed, therefore, to go south. Would it be possible for Theodosia to meet him at some village in the mountains near her house?

Theodosia carried the letter to her husband and handed it to him in silence. When he had read it, he looked up and nodded.

"We'll go, of course," he said. "We can arrange to take Gampy with us."

"But, Joseph, how can you, my dear? With everyone crying out against my father and calling him a murderer, it might ruin your career if you went with me to meet him."

Joseph looked into her anxious eyes, smiling a little. "Very well then," he said, without hesitation, "my career will be ruined."

"But, Joseph . . ." She stopped, silenced by her husband's fingers laid gently across her lips.

"Do you think for one moment, Theo, I'd let you go alone? You know," he went on slowly, "that there are some things about your father I've never altogether understood. I don't suppose anyone understands why he chose to do this frightful thing. Certainly I don't. But that's hardly the question now. What's done is done, and you and I will weather together whatever comes, Theo."

Theodosia looked up at him, tall and straight and steady. She saw the tenderness and loyalty that shone in his eyes.

"Oh, Joseph . . ." She stepped closer, and felt his arms close warm and strong about her. There was no need then of words between them.

The meeting with Mr. Burr was arranged after a good deal of difficulty and delay. Nothing could have made Theodosia realize more sharply the terrible change in her father's life than the pitiful subterfuges that were necessary in planning the visit. It was best, he wrote, that they should meet quietly, in some small town where none of them would be recognized. He had established himself in comfortable obscurity at a certain house in Statesburgh and would await their arrival.

They went at once, traveling the short distance in a carriage driven by Joseph himself. Little Gampy, sitting between them, was greatly excited over the prospect of a visit with Big Gampy. On the way he asked a thousand questions. Would Big Gampy tell him stories? Would he remember to bring the red-painted wagon he had promised he would?

But when they reached the house, Gampy hung back suddenly. Clutching at his mother's skirt, he peered about the dingy, close-smelling hall.

"Mummy"—Gampy's voice rose in a wail—"I don't *like* this place."

For a moment Theodosia's heart failed her. Standing in the dusty, poorly lighted corridor, so strangely out of place in her fashionably cut gown and stylish bonnet, she had a sudden impulse to turn and run away, as if from some horrid, unbelievable dream. Surely her father couldn't be waiting here—in this mean and sordid little place. Her fastidious, proud father, who was never satisfied with anything but the most luxurious and tasteful surroundings. In that moment she had a vision of the long ago evening when she and Natalie had reached the tavern in Albany. The fire on the hearth, and the supper Papa had ordered, the bright nosegay beside each plate and a note to tell them of the dancing party that had been planned for Theodosia's birthday.

"Mummy . . ." The boy tugged at her skirt. "I want to go 'way, Mummy. Big Gampy isn't *here!*"

Quickly Theodosia bent to take the small hand in her own. "Come, darling," she said. Her voice was calm and reassuring as she led him up the narrow, uncarpeted stairs. "We must find Big Gampy."

At the top of the steps a door opened, and Mr. Burr stepped out. He was smiling; his head was high. As he embraced his daughter, then lifted the boy in his arms, Theodosia felt the uncertainty and fear ebbing gradually from her heart. This was her father, as courteous, as composed, as self-possessed as ever. He was talking easily, telling Gampy what a big boy he had grown to be, saying how charming Theodosia looked. No dramatics, no apologies for the mean, shabby little bedroom into which he led them.

Theodosia was aware that beneath the casual manner of his greeting, her father was reaching out to her, seeking to ease her over the difficulty of this meeting. He was telling her, in his own way, not to mind the shabbiness of their surroundings, not to think of all that had happened since they last met, but only of the fact that they were together again. With perfect dignity and grace he was refusing to let this moment he spoiled by any shadow of sorrow or disgrace. But she knew better than to put her gratitude and pride into words.

Instead, kneeling to unfasten the buttons of little Gampy's jacket, she smiled up at her father over the boy's head.

"The rooms seem very nice, Papa," was all she said. But she saw the quick approval that lighted his dark eyes, and she knew that he understood.

When Joseph came up, he found Mr. Burr seated on the floor with little Gampy beside him, while Theodosia looked on, smiling at the boy's raptures over the presents his grandfather had brought.

"Look, Papa—just *look!*" Gampy jumped up to run and take his father's hand. "Big Gampy *did* bring the wagon. And it has wheels that go round; and he brought me a horsy that I can *ride!*"

# ·CHAPTER 17·

# High Treason

THE FEW DAYS of the visit passed quickly and pleasantly.
Mr. Burr devoted himself to Gampy, and kept the boy
in such a state of delight with his stories and songs and won-
derfully exciting new games that Theodosia declared he was
the most superior nursemaid she had ever beheld.

Of his plans for the future Mr. Burr spoke little, but always cheerfully. Even the fact that Richmond Hill was now
gone, having been seized by his creditors, and sold to John
Jacob Astor for twenty-five thousand dollars, to cover a portion of his debts, seemed to dismay him not at all. Richmond
Hill was really too large a place for a lonesome bachelor, he
said. His only regret was that his books had been taken by
the creditors along with all the other furnishings.

"But then," he added, "since it seems fairly certain that
I shall find myself without occupation after the coming
elections, I expect I shall have time and to spare to set about
collecting a new library."

That a new vice-president would be chosen to run with Jefferson for the second term was now a foregone conclusion. And to add one last drop of bitterness to the cup, the new vice-president would be George Clinton of New York, Hamilton's great friend and a lifelong enemy of Burr. The political career of Aaron Burr was ended, people said. He would never again be able to show his face in New York. His law practice was destroyed, for surely no clients would trust themselves to be defended by a man who had been indicted as a murderer. His friends, all but a faithful few, were gone, and his fortune, too—seized by his creditors. There was not a person in New York but believed that Aaron Burr was finished, disgraced, and done forever.

Not a person, that is, but one. Aaron Burr himself.

He might be poor, homeless, and without occupation, but he was never for a moment shaken from his conviction that fortune's wheel would take another turn. When he returned to Washington, he took up his official duties for his few remaining weeks as vice-president as serenely as though nothing had happened. With unperturbed dignity he presided over the Senate. A Washington newspaper reported:

> On Saturday, the 2d of March, Mr. Burr took leave of the Senate. It was said to be one of the most dignified and impressive speeches ever uttered.

Mr. Burr left the Senate with expressions of personal respect, and with prayers and good wishes.

So simple and affecting was the speech that "cheers rang for twenty minutes in the Senate chamber when he had finished speaking, and more than half the audience was in tears." A resolution was at once drawn up, and passed unanimously, "That the thanks of the Senate be presented to Aaron Burr, in testimony of the impartiality, dignity, and ability with which he had ever presided over their deliberations. . . ."

As always, no matter what the public attitude toward him might be, those closest to Burr found much to admire in him. So, without bitterness on either side, he left the Senate chamber that afternoon, having bid a last farewell to his career in public life.

The days following his retirement as vice-president were probably the most crucial in the life of Aaron Burr. Which way would he turn now? What would he do?

There were still a few who believed that he might yet re-establish himself in a position of honor and trust in the public eye. One who clung pathetically to this slim hope was Theodosia. But even though his letters to her in those weeks were full of good cheer, she, reading them, was not altogether deceived. As time went on, it began to be plain even to her tender and loyal heart that her father had flaunted public opinion once too often. All his charm, wit, and imperturbable poise would not, for many a day to come, be likely to blot out the shadow of Hamilton's death.

Even Mr. Burr admitted that to return to his law practice in New York was for the present impossible. He had greatly underestimated the length of public memory, and feeling against him was still so strong that, as he wrote to Joseph:

> In New York I am to be disenfranchised, and in New Jersey hanged. Having substantial objections to both, I

shall not, for the present, hazard either, but shall seek a
new country. . . .

But what country, and where?

What does the irresistible force do when confronted by
an immovable object? Why, the force simply takes a new
direction.

To Theodosia, Mr. Burr wrote of his plans. Immediately
after the fourth of March he would leave Washington and go
to Pittsburgh, there to embark on a curiously bizarre journey. He would board a houseboat, which he had had specially constructed, and he would travel southwest, following
the course of the Ohio River into the Mississippi, and thence
to New Orleans. The prospect of this trip seemed to please
him. It would give him an opportunity to see a new section
of the country, and he expected to stop frequently and visit
various friends who were now settled along the river.

But Theodosia remained anxious and troubled. What,
she wondered, was the object of this strange pilgrimage? Her
father did not say. And who were the friends he spoke of
visiting? His letters mentioned them vaguely, naming only
Andrew Jackson and General Wilkinson, a gentleman of
not altogether savory reputation who was in charge of the
American forces in the Southwest, and who was suspected
by many of being secretly in the employ of Spain.

To make matters worse, the newspapers, which ever
since the duel had reviled and slandered the name of Burr,
treated this latest venture to reams of contemptuous comment, not unmixed with amusement. There was a distinct
flavor of comic opera in the spectacle of the former vice-

president setting out on a houseboat, to float splendidly down a thousand miles of waterway, and in the accounts of the strange cavalcade of Burr and his entourage, the erstwhile villain appeared now as merely a figure of fun.

To Theodosia and Joseph this ridicule was the hardest thing they had yet been called upon to bear. To hold up one's head under tragedy and disgrace is one thing; laughter is quite another.

One morning, over breakfast in the paneled dining room at the Oaks, Joseph flung down his newspaper in disgust.

"Upon my word, Theo," he said, "your father has gone beyond all bounds with this nonsensical voyage. If it's true, as some people think, that he's hatched some sort of plot for gaining political power in the Southwest, then heaven help him. It would be just the chance Jefferson has been waiting for to discredit your father entirely. The Federalists have always hated him. Now with his own party against him, he'd find himself without a single friend in court."

Theodosia made no answer. She turned a fork in her hand, over and over. It was a heavy silver fork—one that her father had given her from Richmond Hill, engraved with the Burr crest.

"God knows, I've tried to understand your father," Joseph went on. "I've admired and respected him—not because he's your father—but because I honestly believed in him. In the Hamilton affair I thought, and still think, that Hamilton was more at fault. I even pitied your father for the accident of circumstances that made everyone turn against him after the duel. But now . . ." He paused and shrugged.

"But now you pity him no longer. Is that it?" Theodosia asked.

"I don't know," Joseph said slowly. "It's hard to pity a man who can never admit he's been mistaken. Your father has so much to make him a great man, Theo. He has brilliance and ambition and energy. And magnificent courage. But he has more pride than any man is entitled to in this world."

Theodosia's hand closed over the fork with its deeply graven crest. "Pride can be a lonely thing, Joseph," she said. "I think if I pity my father for anything, it's for his pride."

But as more time passed, and no new developments came of Mr. Burr's affairs, Theodosia's anxieties grew less. The Alstons' life settled back into untroubled ways. Joseph's work was going well, and as they became more and more engrossed in the busy, pleasant round of days in Charleston, the figure of Aaron Burr faded gradually into the background.

Now, when summer came, there were no more trips to New York. Instead, Joseph took Theodosia and the boy to the mountains again, or to Debordieu Island, where the cool trade winds blew steadily from the sea. Natalie came often to visit, bringing her little Theo to play with Gampy. Then there were long, pleasant days on the beach, while the children built sand castles and paddled in the shallow water, growing brown and sturdy as two young Indians.

They were happy hours for Theodosia, but sometimes, when they all sat together before the blazing pine logs in the cool evenings, a faraway look would come into her eyes and she would watch the flames that leaped and crackled on the hearth. She wondered, then, about her father: when and where they were destined to meet again, and by whose fireside he sat that night.

For many months there was little news from Mr. Burr. Letters came occasionally, but these were mostly comments and instructions to Theodosia for Gampy's first lessons. Now and then a bulky parcel would arrive, with gifts for them all. Feathered Indian headdresses for the boy, and laces and embroideries for Theodosia from the French convents in New Orleans.

Of his own plans and activities he wrote always cheerfully, but in vague terms. By the autumn of 1806 he was on his way north again, traveling by land this time, as he retraced his journey through Tennessee, Kentucky, and Ohio. Again he spoke of visiting friends along the way, and in particular he mentioned a certain Mr. Blennerhassett at whose home, on an island in the Ohio River near Marietta, he had spent a good deal of time.

Joseph frowned over this latest development. But he said nothing to Theodosia of disturbing rumors he had heard in Charleston recently. Rumors of a conspiracy in the Southwest, something about a fantastic plan to conquer Mexico and set up a rival nation on the border of the United States. Rumors in which the names of General Wilkinson and

Blennerhassett figured. Supposing, Joseph thought, Mr. Burr should somehow become involved in this mad scheme? Supposing . . .

There came a day, late that winter, when it was no longer possible for Joseph to keep silent.

It had been a mild afternoon, and Theodosia had driven out in the open carriage, taking young Aaron with her.

As the carriage drew up before the broad front steps of the Oaks, Theodosia gave the boy's shoulder a little pat. "Here we are, Aaron," she said cheerfully. "Out you go, and in to Mammy. We're late for your supper, and I expect we'll both be scolded."

It was not Mammy, but Lottie, who came out the front door and ran down the steps to lift Aaron from the carriage.

"Mr. Alston is in the library, Miss Theodosia," Lottie said. "He says will you come in, please, right away."

Theodosia got out of the carriage quickly. It was odd, she thought, hurrying through the hall and past the dining room. Odd that Joseph should send such a message instead of coming out to meet them himself. She pushed open the library door.

"Joseph . . . ?"

He turned from the window and came straight to her. Then, as if he could not bring himself to speak, he thrust a paper into her hands. "Read this," he said.

She barely glanced at the paper, bewildered by the jumble of strange legal terms.

"I can't understand this, Joseph. Tell me what's happened."

"Your father was arrested, Theo, two weeks ago, by

federal officers, on a charge of high treason. They're bringing him to Richmond for trial. The news just reached Charleston this morning. I can't find out any more than what is printed in the papers, though I've been trying all day."

Theodosia walked over to a sofa and sat down. Slowly, very carefully, she began to draw off her gloves. Papa had sent her these gloves for her birthday last year, she thought. Joseph was talking, trying to explain this puzzling, dreadful thing.

Her father and Mr. Blennerhassett were accused, Joseph was saying, of a plot to separate the southwestern states from the Union. They had raised an armed force in secret, and their plan had been to take possession of Kentucky, Tennessee, and Louisiana and establish the territory as an independent nation. Later they were to invade and conquer Mexico, and there, it was said, Mr. Burr had intended to set himself up as an emperor.

Suddenly, as the meaning of Joseph's words reached her, Theodosia flung aside her gloves and stood up.

"Joseph, *stop!*" Her face was white, but she faced him bravely. "I—I can't let you say these things, Joseph. *Treason* . . . *traitor* . . . these words have nothing to do with my father. My father loves his country, whatever his faults may be. You must know that. You must *believe* it, Joseph."

"Theo, my dearest girl"—Joseph put his hands on her shoulders and looked down into the desperate pleading of her eyes—"I don't know yet what to believe. We can't know the truth until your father has had a chance to explain and defend himself. I'm only trying to tell you what's happened,

Theo. To explain how serious these charges are. God knows," he said gently, "I'd give anything I own to spare you this. Even yet, it may come out all right. Your father will have to prove his innocence, though with the trial in Virginia, Mr. Jefferson's own home state, I wonder——"

"Mr. Jefferson," Theodosia broke in eagerly. "Why, don't you see, Joseph? Mr. Jefferson can help Papa. Surely, if I write him, he'll know best how to straighten out this horrible mistake. I'll write to him, and explain everything . . ."

She crossed to the desk and searched hastily for paper and pen. But before she could begin to write, Joseph's hand closed over hers.

"It's no use, Theo." He drew the pen from her fingers and laid it gently aside. "The order for your father's arrest was signed by President Jefferson."

## ·CHAPTER 18·

# *If It Please the Court*

THE TRIAL OF Aaron Burr for treason was a national sensation. For days, before the arrival of the prisoner, Richmond was seething with excitement. From miles around, people gathered, anxious for a glimpse of this villain who had dared to attempt the most flagrant plot ever uncovered against the United States.

Zachary Taylor was there, and Winfield Scott. Young Washington Irving, who had once been an apprentice in the law office of Mr. Burr, had been sent by a New York newspaper to write articles covering the trial. And General Andrew Jackson came up from Tennessee, to stamp about the corridors of the Old Eagle Tavern in his rough boots and startle the courtly Virginians by proclaiming loudly that his friend Burr had been the victim of trumped-up evidence, manufactured by General Wilkinson and basely used by Jefferson in an attempt to discredit the former Vice-president.

A few voices, here and there, were heard to agree with

Jackson's. But only a few. In general, people were ready to condemn Burr.

"Let's hang the traitor and be done with it," they said angrily.

Probably no man on trial for his life ever walked into a more thoroughly hostile atmosphere than Aaron Burr did on the spring afternoon when he was escorted into the Old Eagle Tavern. But he carried off the moment in true Burr style.

Stepping out of the carriage, he paused to survey the angry, threatening faces that pressed around him. For an instant Mr. Burr hesitated, then, raising his hat, he made a gracious bow and smiled pleasantly.

The crowd shifted uneasily. A current of uncertainty passed through them. This was not what they'd expected at all. They had been prepared for a villain, and here was a man who smiled and bowed and didn't look in the least villainous.

He was small and slight, and it was plain to see he was a gentleman. There was something surprisingly likable about the way he held his head up and looked straight at them.

There was a sudden stir near the tavern door, and General Jackson came out, shouldering his way through the crowd to thrust out a long arm and shake Mr. Burr's hand vigorously.

"Come along inside, sir. Don't let these gawping folk trouble you," Jackson's voice boomed out as he turned to glare at the crowd from under bristling red eyebrows. "They've only come to rubber at the newest curiosity. And don't be worrying about this trial. Three days before any fair court, and I'll guarantee you'll show up the whole thing for what it's worth. A mean, ornery plot against you, cooked up by Jefferson——"

"Take it calmly, Jackson," Mr. Burr's voice broke in with easy good humor. "Save your breath for the jury. I have a presentiment we may need it." With a last amiable nod for the spectators, Mr. Burr turned to follow his guards, and disappeared through the tavern door.

From that day public sentiment toward the prisoner was divided. To many, it still seemed that Burr was guilty. But guilty or no, there was a likable quality about Burr that couldn't be denied. More and more, as days went on, people felt more kindly toward him. He was quiet, he was well-behaved, and no matter how Mr. Hay, the prosecuting attorney, thundered his charges, Mr. Burr only smiled. And the longer the trial dragged on the less serious the charges against him appeared.

The main reason for the delay, which was so fortunate to Burr's cause, was the failure of General Wilkinson to appear in Richmond. He was the chief witness against Burr. The trial could not proceed without him, for it was Wilkinson who had informed Jefferson of the conspiracy, and on his statement depended the proof of Burr's guilty intentions.

And where, people asked of one another, *was* this mysterious Wilkinson? Why wasn't he present in Richmond?

This was the question that dominated the first sessions before the Grand Jury.

Chief Justice John Marshall of the Supreme Court presided over the small courtroom in the State Capitol. It was a little like a circus, those first few days. The room was packed and jammed to overflowing. People stood on chairs and tables, craned over other people's heads and shoulders for a glimpse of the prisoner who sat, with his counsel, at a bench near the rostrum. The Chief Justice had all he could do to maintain decent order. He struck his gavel, again and again, but the crowd simply would not be silent.

Sitting between Edmund Randolph and John Wickham, the lawyers engaged for his defense, Mr. Burr watched the proceedings with a detached and courteous interest. Now and then, when some point of dispute arose, the prisoner would rise, bow politely to Chief Justice Marshall, and offer a suggestion or motion.

There was the increasingly embarrassing absence of General Wilkinson. Again and again, when some point of evidence arose that involved the testimony of the missing Wilkinson, Mr. Burr would inquire, with ironic surprise, *why* Wilkinson was not yet present in Richmond.

Had he not been subpoenaed? He most certainly had.

Had not the prosecution had ample time to fetch their star witness? They most certainly had.

Well, then, Mr. Burr would suggest in his smoothest, most deferential tone, perhaps Mr. Jefferson might know the whereabouts of General Wilkinson.

The point never failed to score.

Gradually the trial began to take on more and more the aspect of a farce. Here was the court, here was the Grand Jury, here was the prisoner. But where was the evidence against him?

Time passed. The trial had been called for early April. Nearly two months passed.

Still no Wilkinson.

Frantic communications passed between Prosecutor Hay and President Jefferson in Washington. How, Mr. Hay demanded, could the President expect him to convict this man Burr when the chief witness and informer against him could not be produced?

At last, on the thirteenth of June, General Wilkinson arrived. But it was too late for the prosecution to work up much confidence in their witness. He blustered and thundered, contradicted himself on a dozen points, and shook his fist accusingly in the direction of the smiling, composed prisoner.

Never had Mr. Burr's natural manner of easy detachment stood him in better stead than now. In contrast to General Wilkinson, Burr's quiet voice, his thorough knowledge of the legal points, made an impression in his favor.

Not that people in general believed Burr to be innocent. It seemed plain enough that he had actually plotted with his friend Blennerhassett to raise an armed force with which they would ultimately march into Mexico and take possession of that territory. Indeed, Mr. Burr himself admitted this. The point of difference between Burr and his accusers lay in the distinction as to just *who* was to profit by his schemes of empire?

Said his accusers: Burr wished to establish himself as dictator of an empire in the Southwest.

Said Burr: Why, no such thing. He had merely meant to acquire the Mexican territory *for* the United States.

Wilkinson's testimony served only to discredit himself, for his own part in the alleged conspiracy was so hopelessly confused that he appeared a fool as well as a rogue. Whereas Mr. Burr was certainly no fool.

Mr. Hay did his best with the case, but the cards were badly stacked against him. Although, eleven days after Wilkinson's appearance, the Grand Jury formally indicted Burr on two counts, treason and misdemeanor, nobody, least of all Mr. Burr himself, took the indictment seriously.

On the morning when it was handed down, and Justice Marshall ordered that the prisoner should now be removed from his comfortable quarters at the Eagle Tavern and confined to the penitentiary, Mr. Burr emerged from the court with his customary smile and bow for the curious crowd, and contented himself by observing, as he stepped into the carriage, that now he was moving to jail, his friends would always find him at home.

So the lengthy trial proceeded again. More visitors than ever arrived in Richmond. The array of witnesses lent a carnival air to the quiet, genteel city. There were raftsmen from the Ohio River barges, planters and politicians from Kentucky and Tennessee, Spaniards from New Orleans, whose swarthy complexions looked fiercely out of place in the mild Virginia landscape.

Justice Marshall, dignified and impartial, presided in the packed courtroom. In spite of his efforts, there was a continual buzz of conversation, particularly from the gallery where the fashionably gowned ladies peered around each others bonnets for a glimpse of the prisoner, and whispered to one another.

"Which one is Burr?"

"The dark one, at the table there. With the black coat and white stock."

"Oh! . . . Very *handsome,* isn't he? I suppose that's Wilkinson, the gray-haired one with the shifty eye. Revolting-looking creature."

"Shh, listen. Burr is getting up to say something."

In the midst of the trial Mr. Burr produced his greatest surprise. If it please the court, Mr. Burr asked permission to subpoena one more witness in his own defense.

Justice Marshall nodded. Who was it the defendant wish to call?

Mr. Burr would like to subpoena Thomas Jefferson, President of the United States, and demand that he produce, as material evidence, certain papers, now in his possession, relating directly to General Wilkinson's part in the alleged conspiracy for which Mr. Burr was being tried.

There was a gasp of astonishment from the spectators. Then a burst of excited comment. Fancy Burr daring to ask that the President be called in *defense* of the prisoner.

Mr. Hay was on his feet at once, protesting angrily that Mr. Burr's request was brazen impudence, and deserved a rebuke as such.

But Justice Marshall, rapping sternly for order, leaned across the desk to ask a question. Was Mr. Burr reliably informed that these papers were actually in the possession of Mr. Jefferson?

Mr. Burr was. He was likewise positive that they bore directly upon the case in hand, and would shed considerable light on the value of General Wilkinson's testimony.

A pause, while the Justice considered. Then in a sober, unemotional voice, Marshall gave his decision. Under the circumstances, he could see no reason why the President should not be served with a subpoena, and ordered to produce the papers in question.

Further sensation among the spectators. This was amazing, truly—and wholly without precedent.

Mr. Hay, his face very red, sat down. He was heard by those near him to observe bitterly, "Burr must be inspired by the devil himself to know about those papers!"

Whatever his inspiration, Mr. Burr proved to be right. Jefferson was duly subpoenaed, and although he was excused from appearing in person at the trial, he was compelled to send the papers as evidence. And quite as Burr had asserted, they shed a new and unfavorable light on the reliability of Wilkinson's testimony.

Mr. Burr's defense of his own actions was simple, and disarmingly candid. He had purchased a good deal of land in Louisiana, during his visit in New Orleans. He freely admitted that he had conferred with his friend Blennerhassett on the possibility of organizing a group of men to settle this land. The two men, encouraged by General Wilkinson, had discussed the possibility of mobilizing their settlers into a sort of private army, for the purpose of taking over a portion of Mexico, now belonging to Spain.

But—and here Mr. Burr was very emphatic—they had at no time considered or even mentioned any plan to sever any states from the Union.

A fantastic, storybook sort of explanation, to be sure. But still it *was* an explanation. Any way you looked at it, people said, the Mexican venture had been a thoroughly wild scheme. And when it was brought out in evidence that the total armed forces which the defendant had mustered consisted of some fifty-odd adventurers, owning, among them, a dozen rifles, the whole thing appeared more ridiculous than ever.

As for Wilkinson, it was now plain to be seen that his reasons for disclosing the alleged plot to Jefferson had been prompted by nothing more than his own dissatisfaction with the share of the "proceeds" allotted to him by Burr.

So the weeks passed, each day's evidence establishing more and more surely the fact that neither the accusers nor the accused deserved any particular respect, and that Jefferson—the great Jefferson—had been fooled by the rascally Wilkinson.

Except for Justice Marshall and the unfortunate Mr. Hay, no one took anything pertaining to the trial very seriously any more. Certainly, the prisoner, after the first tense weeks, appeared to be rather enjoying himself.

·CHAPTER 19·

# The Hour of Noon

BUT TO THEODOSIA, in Charleston, the weeks that passed
so quickly and in such excitement in Richmond were
a different story. She had only two sources of information
as to how the trial progressed: the newspapers, with their
lurid accounts of the proceedings at Richmond, and her
father's letters.

These, to be sure, were cheerful enough. But then he
was always cheerful, and she knew from long and bitter
experience that his efforts to minimize anything unfavorable
to himself were by no means always to be trusted. Letters,
such as the one in which he described his new "lodgings"
in the Richmond jail, brought her small comfort, for all the
lightheartedness of his tone:

> I have three rooms in the third floor of the penitentiary
> [he wrote] making an extent of one hundred feet. My
> jailer is quite a polite and civil man—altogether unlike
> the idea one would form of a jailer. You would have
> laughed to hear our compliments the first evening.

Jailer: I hope, sir, it would not be disagreeable to you if I should lock this door after dark.

Burr: By no means, sir; I should prefer it, to keep out intruders.

Jailer: It is our custom, sir, to extinguish all lights at nine o'clock; I hope, sir, you will have no objection to conform to that.

Burr: That, sir, I am sorry to say, is impossible; for I never go to bed till twelve, and always burn two candles.

Jailer: Very well, sir, just as you please. I should have been glad if it had been otherwise; but, as you please, sir.

While I have been writing different servants have arrived with messages, notes, and inquiries, bringing oranges, lemons, pineapples, raspberries, apricots, cream, butter, ice and some ordinary articles.

That Mr. Burr was aware of the sober side of this proceeding, and of the pain and anxiety Theodosia was suffering, was shown in a briefer and quite different passage written to her a few days later.

He had urged her to come to Richmond and be present at the trial. She had hesitated. He guessed that the reason for her reluctance was her dread of seeing him in a position of humiliation—the accused prisoner before the court. Very kindly and understandingly, he let her know that she need fear no such painful spectacle.

. . . I should never invite anyone, much less those so dear to me, to witness my disgrace. . . . I cannot be humiliated or disgraced. If absent, you will suffer great solicitude. In my presence you will feel none. . . .

Nevertheless, Theodosia continued to feel bitterly the shame of the position in which her father now found himself. That he, who had served his country as a soldier of the

Revolution, who had only a few years ago narrowly missed being elected to the presidency itself, should now be brought before a court and charged with high treason was the cruelest blow she had ever suffered. To see her father who had had such a wealth of opportunities before him—who might, if only fate and his own nature had varied *ever so slightly,* have attained the greatest honor and dignity—reduced to hoping at best for a dubious victory, following a shamefully shabby trial, cut her to the heart.

Finally it was arranged that Joseph should visit Mr. Burr in Richmond. He returned a few weeks later to report to Theodosia that her father's health and spirits were excellent.

"On my word, Theo," Joseph said, in an odd mixture of despair and amusement, "your father is the hero of Richmond. His rooms in the penitentiary are a great deal more like a fashionable apartment than a jail. Visitors come and go all day. The best families in Richmond send their servants with baskets of flowers, and hampers of home-cooked foods. You never saw such an assortment. Roasted birds, cakes and pies, and so many bottles of the choicest wines that your father says he'll soon have to petition the jailer for the use of the cellar to store them in."

Theodosia shook her head with a sigh. "I don't like it, Joseph," she said.

"Nor do I," Joseph answered soberly. "I couldn't help but admire his courage. But a man can defy his fate just so far. I've wondered sometimes whether perhaps the shock of the duel and all the trouble that followed may not have changed your father more than he realizes."

"Sometimes," Theodosia said slowly, "I've wondered, too." She was silent for a moment. "If only we could do something to help him, to bring him back to himself . . ."

"I think, perhaps, if you would be willing to go to Richmond . . ." Joseph hesitated, seeing the quick look of distress in his wife's eyes. "I know it's asking a great deal of you, Theo. But still, your father is on trial for his life."

Theodosia looked up. "I do want to go, Joseph," she said quietly. "It's been selfish of me to refuse, simply because I dreaded to see my father a prisoner. If he needs me, I shan't hesitate any longer."

Within a few days they were packing to leave for Richmond. It was arranged that Natalie should come and stay at the Oaks while they were gone. It was the first time Theodosia had really been separated from her son, and she pressed a thousand anxious directions on Natalie.

"You *will* be careful about his food, won't you, Natalie?" Theodosia said for the twentieth time. "He's always been dreadfully susceptible to fevers. Oh, dear, if I could only divide myself in half, and send one part to Richmond while the other half stayed here."

Natalie was comfortingly certain that all would be well. "Since you must remain all in one piece, Theo, it's Papa who needs you just now far more than young Aaron. And, Theo, you won't forget to give Papa my dearest love? And write me exactly how things are going?"

The night before the Alstons reached Richmond, they stopped at an inn in Fayetteville. Theodosia found a note from her father waiting.

Under no circumstances, her father wrote, was she to allow herself the slightest twinge of sentimental pity or concern on his account:

> . . . I beg and expect it of you that you will conduct yourself as becomes my daughter, and that you manifest no signs of weakness or alarm. Remember, no agitations, no complaints, no fears and anxieties on the road, or I renounce thee.

Just as on that other occasion, in the dingy little inn at Statesburgh, Theodosia resolved to met him with the dignity he required of her. When they arrived next afternoon in Richmond, and drove directly to the penitentiary, her head was lifted proudly. There was in her manner no slightest hint that she looked forward to the meeting with anything but pleasant anticipation.

John Prevost was at the door to greet them. "It's good to see you, Theo-mio." John's round, cheerful face shone with brotherly affection. "And, my word, how handsome you look. Come along upstairs. Papa is in the greatest wax of impatience, waiting for your arrival. He's sent me down at least a dozen times in the last hour to watch for your carriage."

"John, how is he?" A shadow came into Theodosia's eyes.

"Never better," John said quickly. He tucked her hand beneath his arm and turned to lead her up the steps and into the gray stone corridor. "Only one thing has troubled him, and that's been his concern for you. But one glance will be enough to show him that his Theo hasn't the slightest intention of pining away."

If one thing more had been needed to sway the balance of popular opinion in favor of Mr. Burr, the appearance of Theodosia in Richmond accomplished it. Already people were disposed to *like* the prisoner. For Theodosia they went one step further: they *trusted* her completely. Her appearances in the courtroom, where she sat quietly in the gallery, observing the proceedings with an air of gentle dignity, did more for her father's cause than all the array of witnesses who were called to testify in his behalf.

But for the most part she wisely refrained from attending the hearings. While Joseph went each morning, to sit with Mr. Burr and his attorneys, Theodosia was busy attending to her borrowed household. Daily she visited her father's rooms in what he called his "town house" and saw that everything there was arranged for his comfort. Nearly every evening she and Joseph and John were permitted to dine with Mr. Burr, and in the pleasant companionship of the little family circle they seemed to forget that barred windows cast a grim shadow of doubt over the future.

Never for one moment did Mr. Burr allow that shadow to depress them. Theodosia wrote to Natalie that her father had seldom been in better spirits. How much of his good humor was assumed for their sakes, she added, even she couldn't guess.

On the morning of Tuesday, the first of September, Theodosia was in her small first-floor sitting room. The day before, Justice Marshall had directed the jury to retire and consider its verdict on the guilt or innocence of Aaron Burr.

It was a fair morning, bright with a warm sun that streamed in the front windows and shone across the desk where Theodosia sat writing to her brother Frederic and his wife. She was alone. Joseph had gone to court as usual.

"You must go, of course, Joseph," Theodosia had insisted. "If the decision is favorable, I'm quite willing to wait a little longer for the good news. And if the verdict should go against Papa"—she paused—"he'll need you far more than I."

She sat now, writing steadily, while the small gilt clock on the mantel ticked away the minutes in the quiet room. The outcome, she wrote, was as yet unknown, but whatever it might be, she believed that somehow, in some place, her father's name would still be freed from the shadow of the word "traitor." As for herself and Joseph and John, they were all well. People in Richmond had been kindness itself, showing her "the most delicate attentions and sympathy."

The clock whirred, making ready to strike the hour of noon. Any moment now, she thought, the word might come. The last chiming note died into silence, and there was a loud knock at the door.

Theodosia rose. From the back of the house she could hear a servant coming to answer the door, but she did not wait. The silk folds of her skirt rustled lightly as she hurried into the hall.

A strange youth, standing on the doorstep, looked up at her curiously.

"Mrs. Alston?"

"Yes."

"A message for you, ma'am. From Mr. Burr."

She took the paper and opened it with steady fingers. In her father's meticulous hand, was written:

> The jury has brought in a verdict. Not guilty. God bless thee.
>
> A. Burr

·CHAPTER 20·

# *Farewell*

ON THEIR RETURN to Charleston, the Alstons found
that young Aaron had been ill for ten days before
their arrival. It was nothing serious, Natalie assured them.
She'd called Dr. Logan at once, and he had said it was the
fever again, and put the boy to bed on a diet of thin gruel
and barley water.

Fevers, after all, were to be expected in this season.
Scarcely a child in the South escaped them, and parents
learned to accept philosophically the sight of plump, rosy
cheeks turned pale, and small bodies grown thin and languid.

Nevertheless, Theodosia and Joseph were alarmed, and
for the first few days after their home-coming they had no
thought for anything but their son. Little by little he began
to improve.

"Tell me about Big Gampy, Mum," he asked one day.
"Why didn't he come home with you?"

"Because he had to go north, dear. On business. But he

sent you all sorts of messages and a wonderful surprise I've been keeping until you felt stronger."

Theodosia went to fetch a box of lead soldiers, gaily painted, and began to set them up on the bed.

"See how fine and brave they look, Aaron." She smiled, remembering the day her father had left the courtroom after his acquittal, and how he had driven, the first thing, to a shop in Richmond to hunt out a gift for his grandson. "These soldiers on horseback are the cavalry, and this one in the cocked hat is their colonel."

"Like my grandfather was in the war," Aaron said eagerly. He propped himself up on one thin elbow to examine the little lead officer in his blue-painted coat. "Will Big Gampy be coming to visit later, Mum? When his business is finished?"

"I hope so, dear. But it may not be right away. He's thinking of taking a long trip. To England, perhaps, and France, where Natalie used to live."

"Oh!" The boy dropped back against the pillow. "France is awfully far away. Natalie says it took days and days to come from there."

"Yes, I know. But wherever Gampy is, no matter how far away, he's always thinking of us, Aaron. You must remember that."

By the time winter came Aaron was quite well. Dr. Logan assured Theodosia that she had no more cause to worry about him. "Let the boy start riding next week," he advised, "and keep him outdoors as much as you can. We'll soon have him as good as new again."

In the late spring Theodosia learned that her father was
to sail for England within the month. All his friends advised
him, and he agreed, that it was best for him to be out of
the country for the time being. How long he might be absent, he could not say. But he must go.

Theodosia began at once to make plans for a trip to New
York. Although her father had carefully refrained from
asking her to come, she sensed, for the first time, a certain
loneliness in him. And she felt that they must have the comfort of one last brief visit together before he set out on the
long journey.

Joseph agreed. But since his work would keep him in
the legislature, Theodosia sailed alone from Charleston. Six
days later she was in New York.

She soon discovered the extent of the bitter humiliation
her father had endured since the September afternoon when
they had parted in Richmond. Even though the court had
acquitted him, the shadow of disgrace still hung over him.
And though he remained self-possessed and calm as ever,
she saw in their first meeting that his old bravado was shaken.

Joseph had once said, "A man can defy his fate just so
far." Now, it seemed, the fate that Aaron Burr had for so
long refused to admit or accept had caught up with him at
last. No man can live without making mistakes, but Mr.
Burr, for all his brilliance and ability, had chosen his mistakes
with peculiarly disastrous genius. The very qualities which
had once made him strong—his stubborn independence, his
reckless scorn for public opinion, above all, his fatal pride—
had made him seem almost invulnerable. But there had been
no provision in his iron code for the possibility of defeat,

and now that defeat had come it was too late to change.

Again, Theodosia reflected sadly, it was Joseph who had said, "It's hard to pity a man who can never admit he's been mistaken." Long ago Aaron Burr had chosen to walk alone. And now, except for a handful of friends who remained loyal, he must be content to travel his way—alone.

The debts which he had accumulated over the years, with such a blandly cheerful disregard for the day of reckoning, now rose up like angry ghosts to torment him. Even though it was commonly known that he was financially ruined, his harrying creditors pursued him, determined, at least, that he shouldn't escape the country a free man.

Because of these creditors, and their relentless efforts to throw her father into the debtor's court, Theodosia was forced to meet him secretly—here for an hour, there for a few minutes—always at night and under a cover of mystery and subterfuge that grieved and dismayed her.

Early in June the packet boat *Clarissa* lay at anchor in the Narrows of New York harbor, awaiting a fair wind to set sail for England. A passage had been engaged in the name of Mr. G. H. Edwards, for a gentleman who was to share a modest cabin with three strangers.

Late on the night of June sixth, a skiff was rowed out from the Long Island shore to where the *Clarissa* rode the quiet sea under a calm, starlit sky. A rather small man, something over middle age, to judge from his appearance, left the skiff and came aboard the *Clarissa* where he was met, as prearranged, by the captain.

"Mr. Edwards?"

"Yes."

"Good evening, sir. Everything has been arranged, I hope to your satisfaction."

"I'm very grateful, captain." The small man bowed. "My wants will be very simple, I assure you."

"Your instructions have been carefully followed. No one but myself has been informed of your presence."

"Excellent. When do you plan to sail, captain?"

"At dawn, if the wind holds. Is there anything I can do to make you comfortable before you go to your cabin, Mr. Edwards?"

"Only one favor, if it's not too much trouble." The small man drew a letter from his pocket. "I should be very grateful if this could be sent ashore by the pilot boat in the morning. It's to go to Mrs. Joseph Alston. The address is noted."

On the morning of June seventh, Theodosia woke early. She rose at once and went to the window that faced south, across the trees and promenade of Battery Park to the harbor dotted with ships. Anxiously, her eyes searched the horizon for the spot where, for the past week, the *Clarissa* had been visible. There was nothing there now. Only an empty stretch of blue water glittered beneath the early summer sun. "Farewell, Papa," Theodosia whispered softly. "Farewell."

Then she dressed quickly, and went to the desk where a package of folded papers lay. The evening before, her father had given them to her, with instructions. They were notes and accounts representing various sums of money due him.

"Contrary to the general opinion," he had said with an

odd smile, "I not only borrowed considerable money, but also, on occasion, lent it. You'll find the notes here, duly signed and witnessed. Also a number of uncollected fees from my formerly grateful law clients. If you can manage to raise any portion of the cash, and forward it to me, it will be useful. I'm asking you to do it, instead of John or Van Ness, because the people who owe me are mostly your friends. No lawyer would stand a ghost of a chance of collecting the money, with me out of the country. But an appeal from you, I think, they will scarcely dare to refuse. Believe me, Theo," he had added, "I dislike asking such a disagreeable favor of you, but, at present, it seems that fate leaves me little choice in anything."

Selecting two or three of the more promising accounts, Theodosia rose from the desk. She had slept poorly, and a dull, nagging ache throbbed miserably behind her eyes. Nevertheless, she put on her best mantle of blue silk, and adjusted a small velvet-trimmed hat to just the proper tilt.

At the first office, that of a prominent judge who, in years past, had often dined at Richmond Hill, Theodosia was asked to wait in the dim, walnut-paneled anteroom. This wasn't going to be too bad, after all, she thought. There couldn't be anything very terrifying, surely, in talking to the judge, whom she remembered as a kindly, whiskered gentleman interested in horses and sailing.

When the clerk came back, she stood up quickly.

But instead of showing her in, the young man began to speak rapidly, his pale eyes never quite meeting hers. He was extremely sorry, it was *most* unfortunate that the judge happened to be, on this particular morning, unusually pressed for time. He sent his warmest compliments to Mrs. Alston. In the meantime, if there were anything the clerk might do . . . or if she cared to leave a message . . .

Theodosia took up her gloves and handbag. She was grateful for the judge's kindness, but there was no message.

The young man leaped to open the door for her, and bowed with effusive, nervous politeness as she walked swiftly past him and down the worn, wooden steps.

Once in the street, she stood for a moment as if uncertain which way to turn. All about her, people moved with quick, purposeful steps, intent upon the business that carried them in and out of the red-brick office buildings that lined Wall Street. Though the sun was high now and waves of heat rose shimmeringly from the cobbled pavement, Theodosia felt a shiver pass through her and drew the light silk of her mantle closer.

Then, opening her handbag, she glanced at the address on the second paper. It was a number in Maiden Lane.

For days Theodosia continued to make her weary rounds. In one anteroom after another she waited, with patient dignity, for some young clerk to return with a message. Occasionally the men she sought would see her. They would greet her with friendly courtesy, and talk cordially enough until she broached the subject of her father's accounts. Then their smiles would grow thin, or vanish altogether, and they would speak vaguely of troubled times, and many commitments which, to their regret, made any immediate action quite impossible. Perhaps, if Mrs. Alston would return some time in the future . . .

Toward the end of the month, Theodosia left the city and went to visit Frederic and his wife in Pelham. There, in the cool quiet of the country, where the water lapped peacefully along the curving shore, she could forget for a while the long procession of dim, paneled office anterooms and the apologetic faces of pale young clerks.

But Frederic was alarmed by the deep shadows of weariness that ringed her eyes.

"You've got to stop this, Theo," he said firmly when she told him what she had been attempting to do. "Father would a thousand times rather starve—though you may be sure it won't come to that—than have you wearing yourself out on his account."

"But I must try a little longer, Frederic. I shall write some letters while I'm here. Perhaps that's a better plan than calling in person. And it isn't as if I were asking favors. These people owe Papa money. Every one of them."

Frederic shook his head and sighed. "Just now," he said slowly, "anything connected with the name of Burr is a doomed cause. The sooner you realize that the better. Besides, you'll make yourself ill going on like this. Already you look as dragged out as a drowned kitten."

"Oh, surely, Frederic, not that bad." She smiled. "I'm not ill, only tired. And I think, for the first time in my life, a little homesick."

The letters over which she worked so long and patiently brought no better results. At length, worn out with strain and discouragement, and desperately lonely for Joseph and Aaron, she began to feel feverish and miserable. Writing to her father one day, she was forced to admit that all her efforts to collect his money had utterly failed.

> Except myself, all your friends are well. But the world begins to cool terribly around me. You would be surprised how many I supposed attached to me have abandoned the sorry, losing game of disinterested friendship. Frederic and John alone, however, are worth a host. Adieu once more . . .

Only John came to see Theodosia off on the morning when she sailed from New York. Looking back to where he stood on the pier, waving his hat, she could hear him calling to her cheerfully above the clanging confusion of harbor sounds.

"Good-by, Theo-mio. Get well soon, and my love to young Aaron. Don't forget."

"Good-by, dear John."

Tears of weakness were in her eyes as she stood by the rail later, watching the shore line of New York gradually recede. It seemed almost a strange city to her now, somehow different. Yet nothing had really changed at all. The spire of old Trinity still rose, straight and slim, above the peaked roofs, and somewhere, just out of sight beyond the curving shore, the green lawns of Richmond Hill still sloped down to the fringe of willows that bordered on the broad, blue river.

A fair wind was with them nearly all the way to Charleston. It was late afternoon, getting on toward dusk, when they dropped anchor in the harbor and the passengers gathered on deck to look for familiar faces among those who waited on the dock. None searched more eagerly than Theodosia.

Suddenly she leaned over the rail to wave excitedly, and the other passengers, who had observed her during the voyage, always alone, reading or looking sadly out to sea, were surprised now to see how very young and pretty she looked.

A few minutes later Theodosia was going down the gangplank. Joseph hurried toward her and young Aaron, in a new blue suit and sailor hat, hurled himself upon his mother with a joyful shout.

"Oh, Aaron, *darling,* how huge you look! You must have grown inches while I was gone. And Joseph . . ." Theodosia straightened and turned, smiling with all her heart, as his arms, strong and sure, held her close.

"Oh, Joseph—Joseph," she whispered against his shoulder. "You can't possibly know how *good* it is to come home."

## CHAPTER 21

# Christmas Eve

I T WAS CHRISTMAS EVE in Charleston, and a light, wet snow was falling. Down through the gaunt, black cypress trees it drifted, frosting the strands of Spanish moss until they sparkled like lace in the light of a misty moon.

On a hill, just outside the town, stood the Orphanage where the boys and girls, who were young Dr. Logan's special charges, were in the midst of a Christmas feast. The bare dining room, with its long wooden tables, had been trimmed with bright festoons of holly, and each of the small guests wore a gay paper hat that contrasted oddly with the plain gray stuff of the little boys' suits and the girls' sober frocks of serviceable brown cambric.

At the head table, next to Dr. Logan, Theodosia sat smiling down the long line of happy, well-scrubbed faces. Small fists were busily stuffing away quantities of roast turkey.

"I do wish Joseph could be here to see the children," Theodosia said. "He sent especially to the plantation for the turkeys. But at the last minute some visitors arrived from Washington on business, and he had to receive them."

"It was good of you to come and bring Aaron." The doctor smiled. "I was afraid my young ones might be shy with him at first, but from the looks of things he seems to have made friends without much trouble."

Theodosia glanced down the table to where her son was devouring his dinner as eagerly as any, talking meanwhile, through a mouthful of turkey, to a little girl beside him.

"There's one thing to be said for Aaron," she said laughingly. "He's never at a loss for words. I expect that's what comes of having a father and a grandfather in politics, not to mention all his ancestors who were preachers."

After supper they trimmed the Christmas tree. Whatever shyness the children might still have felt in the presence of the visitors vanished entirely at the sight of the huge hampers, crammed with good things, that Theodosia knelt down to unpack. There were figs and dates, walnuts and cinnamon sticks, and enough striped peppermints, Theodosia said, to guarantee a hundred stomach-aches the following morning.

Each child, from the tallest, gangling boy to one baby girl who could scarcely walk, had a turn at putting his own bit of decoration on the tree. When they had finished, the broad green branches had all but disappeared beneath garlands of strung popcorn and scarlet cranberries.

There were games for another hour, and while the children romped and shouted through Blind Man's Bluff and

London Bridge Is Falling Down, Theodosia and the doctor stood together near the big fireplace where the pine logs crackled.

After a few minutes, Theodosia spoke hesitantly. "I have one more surprise for the children, Dr. Logan, but first I wanted to ask your approval. Some weeks ago I wrote to my father, and happened to mention the Orphanage, and the work you were doing with the children here. Yesterday I had an answer from him, written from Paris, and enclosing a check. He said it would make him very happy if you would divide it among the children, so that each one would have a little pocket money of his own to spend as he chooses. I"— she paused uncertainly, and then went on, her voice very low—"I don't know what sort of things you may have heard of my father, but I've brought the check—in case you care to accept it."

Dr. Logan took the slip of paper. "People say many things about Mr. Burr," he said slowly, "but nothing I hear in the future will ever make me forget this. I can guess what it meant to him to send this gift. Most of these children have never had a penny of their own to spend. I dare say your father guessed that. Shall I tell them who sent the money, Mrs. Alston?"

Theodosia shook her head. "Just say it came from someone very far away," she said.

On the way home that night Theodosia and Aaron heard the bells of St. Michael's chiming the hour as they turned into King Street where the damp snow had clung to the iron grillwork on the balconies of the tall brick houses, making them look like patterns of spun sugar.

"Ten o'clock," Theodosia said. "It's quite scandalously late for you to be out, sir. But I hope you had a good time."

Aaron wriggled comfortably under the fur rug beside her. "I had three helps of turkey, Mum, but that wasn't the most. One of the other boys had four. I wish I could play up there every day. I like the children much better than the ones I know."

"I like them, too. Suppose we ask Dr. Logan to bring some of the boys and girls to the house someday soon. And later, in the spring, we might have a picnic at the Oaks for all of them. Do you know"—she looked out the carriage window—"it almost looks as if we might have a white Christmas as we used to in New York. Then we had sleighs instead of carriages, and the horses had bells on their harnesses so the whole city would sound like a jingling music box. When I was a little girl I'd stay awake just to listen to them. My nurse was always cross about it. She said sleigh bells were nonsense. But then"—she laughed—"Nanny always thought things that were fun were nonsense."

"I guess all nurses are the same." Aaron sighed. "I'm awfully glad I'm almost nine now, and don't have to have Mammy any more. I always liked you and Papa much better than I liked Mammy."

"Did you, Aaron?"

"Oh, yes." After a moment he added. "You always let me have more sweets, you see."

When Aaron had been put to bed, Theodosia went into

her sitting room across the hall. Joseph was still busy with the visitors downstairs. She could hear their voices as she crossed the landing.

She paused by the desk, half intending to write her father a description of the Christmas supper at the Orphanage, telling him how gratefully Dr. Logan had received his gift for the children. Instead she went to the window and stood looking out across the low rooftops to the harbor, black and still beneath a starless sky.

Since the night her father had boarded the *Clarissa,* she had had letters from England, Sweden, Germany, and now from Paris. Cheerful letters for the most part, telling of his travels, of the people he had met, and the houses where he had been entertained. When he mentioned, rarely, the difficulties of being an exile in strange countries, perpetually embarrassed by lack of money, it was always in a light vein, twisting the stories so as to make them into amusing anecdotes for her.

She had one comfort in the fact that Vanderlyn was also abroad, and spent much of his time with Mr. Burr. And from Vanderlyn's letters she drew a much clearer picture of her father's actual existence. It was true that he was obliged to live in the most meager style, Vanderlyn replied to her anxious query. But poverty, he assured her, was by no means an unfashionable state in Paris. Mr. Burr had kept his health and good spirits. Indeed, he had made so many friends that wherever one went in Paris one was more than likely to find "Monsieur le Colonel Burr" surrounded by an affectionate and admiring circle.

Vanderlyn himself was having a considerable success.

His painting, "The Ruins of Carthage," exhibited in the Salon of 1808, was awarded the highest of all honors, the gold medal of the Emperor Napoleon, who took occasion to compliment the artist in person.

Theodosia smiled, a trifle ruefully, over this news, remembering the first afternoon when she and Vanderlyn had met, and his troubled confession of his doubts that he should ever live up to Mr. Burr's expectations. Now he had justified his patron's faith brilliantly, but fortune had twisted things about so oddly that the first proceeds of Vanderlyn's success went to buy a supply of firewood, rice, potatoes, as well as other food and a much-needed greatcoat, for Mr. Burr, who had once done so much for him.

So long as Vanderlyn and his other friends in Paris were near, Theodosia was confident that her father would be looked after as faithfully and generously as his pride would allow. But still she grieved for him. The thought of his exile and the disgrace that prevented his return to America was the one blight in the peaceful contentment of her life.

Looking out now over the dark waters of the harbor, she heard the church bells toll the hour of eleven. One hour more, and it would be Christmas. A message, unspoken, went from her heart across the lonely black ocean.

"Merry Christmas, Papa—Merry Christmas."

"Theo . . ."

Theodosia turned to see Joseph. "What's happened?" she asked curiously. "You look as if you were fairly bursting with news of some sort."

"Do I?" Joseph laughed, but the next minute a sober

expression came into his deep-blue eyes. "Theo, those men came direct from Washington. They say there's no doubt about it. We shall be at war with England before the new year is out. Things can't go on as they are now. Our ships are being raided constantly, and the crews and cargoes interned. I've dreaded the thought of war. But if it comes, our country must be united, and prepared to defend itself." He paused. "Theo . . ."

"Yes?"

"They came tonight to ask me to run for governor of the state."

"What did you tell them, Joseph?"

"I said I would."

Theodosia looked up at him, pride and tenderness shining in her dark eyes.

Late that night Theodosia lay awake. Outside the wind had shifted, turning the wet snow into rain that pattered gently against the windows. So Aaron wouldn't wake up to see his first white Christmas, after all.

Lying very still, Theodosia thought of what Joseph had told her. If war was really coming, perhaps, at last, the bitterness against her father would be forgotten, pushed aside by the confusion of a thousand more pressing concerns. If only she could help him to come home before the war began. . . . There must be *something* she could do. There must be someone she could appeal to, someone who would understand and help her. Someone, somewhere, who would know how to break down the barriers that still kept her father from coming back to America.

It was three o'clock on Christmas morning when Theodosia rose and went into the sitting room to light a candle on the desk. She shivered a little, drawing her warm robe closer, as she dipped her pen.

She hesitated at first, wondering how to begin the letter. It had been years since she had had a word from Dolley Madison. James Madison was President now, and the cheerful, friendly Dolley lived in the White House, surrounded by all the dignity and caution of being the President's wife. But Dolley had spoken once, on a morning long ago in Richmond Hill. "I shan't ever forget all your father's kindnesses. . . . I hope I may pay him back someday," she had said.

Theodosia dipped her pen again and commenced to write:

Madam:

You may perhaps be surprised at receiving a letter from one with whom you have had so little intercourse in the past years. But your surprise will cease when you recall that my father, once your friend, is now in exile. . . .

·CHAPTER 22·

# A Gold Watch

DOLLEY MADISON HAD not forgotten.

And the first lady, moreover, knew a thing or two about getting her way with "the little Madison." To Theodosia's long, touchingly humble, and eloquent letter, she made no direct reply, perhaps because she had been warned that Joseph knew nothing of Theodosia's plea. Whatever may have been the means of persuasion employed upon the President, they had their effect.

A few weeks after Theodosia had written, wheels were set in motion to provide a passport for Mr. Burr, and a guarantee that no further legal action would be taken against him upon his return.

But the wheels moved slowly. And weary lengths of red tape had to be unwound before the day when, at last, the American ambassador in Paris delivered the final necessary paper into the hands of Mr. Burr.

Even then, there were more delays and difficulties to be faced. First, the perpetually vexing problem of money.

"And the problem of money," said Mr. Burr to Vander-lyn, "is that there *is* no money."

He must raise the money needed for his passage home. He sold nearly all of his books; Vanderlyn was willing to contribute as much as his slender treasury would allow, but still there was not enough. At the last moment Mr. Burr offered for sale a small gold watch. A very fine watch, in a case most beautifully chased. Engraved inside were the words: *For Aaron Burr Alston, with his grandfather's love.*

During the long months in Paris, Mr. Burr had more than once scrimped on his dinner, or shivered in his room without a fire, for the sake of adding a few more sous to the fund he was saving toward the little watch. On the day it was sold he wrote to Theodosia:

> . . . I have raised the money by the sale of all my little possessions and loose property. Among others, alas! my dear Gamp's watch. . . . After turning it over, and looking at it, and opening it, and putting it to my ear like a baby, and begging you a thousand pardons, the beautiful little watch—was sold.

But though her father grieved over the loss of his treasure, to Theodosia only one thing counted now. Her father was coming home.

She had word that he would sail for Boston in the last week of September. More than a month passed, a month of joyful anticipation while she waited for the news of his arrival. Then a letter came, not from Boston, but England.

His ship had been overtaken by a British frigate two days after sailing, and put back into a British port where the passengers and crew were unceremoniously dumped.

Now there were fresh reams of red tape to be waded through. Permissions, passports, and papers had to be granted all over again. And new passage money must be raised. The last treasures held in reserve for Theodosia, must be sold. Mr. Burr wrote:

> Got some things out of my trunk to sell . . . a length of velvet which I had sealed up for you, and resolved to keep through thick and thin. But everything visible must go, or I shall lose the opportunity of the ship. . . . Found some ribbons I had bought for you at the Palais Royal. After gazing at them, and painting to myself the pleasure they would give, I reluctantly resolved to sell them. . . . Thus I am obliged to plunder you and Gampillo to the last article.

In March, 1812, Mr. Burr finally sailed from Liverpool on the ship *Aurora*. After five stormy weeks, he landed in Boston. A few days later he had sold his last precious half-dozen books to Dr. Kirkland, the president of Harvard University, and was on his way to New York, where he arrived one bright June morning, exactly four years from the night the *Clarissa* had sailed from the harbor.

It was, however, a very different city to which he now returned.

War was in the air and with the whole populace united to arm itself, there was no time for old grudges. The grievances against Mr. Burr, which had once seemed so important, faded before more pressing concerns. Indeed, it was felt by many that Burr had, perhaps, been *too* harshly treated, after all. Time had passed, tempers had cooled. Here was a man who, no matter what his faults, had taken his punishment bravely. Let him be forgiven, and no hard feelings.

Nothing, probably, could have surprised Mr. Burr more than such a mellow reception. But he accepted good fortune with precisely the same philosophic good temper with which he had borne the years of disgrace.

"If it takes a war to make people change their minds about me," Mr. Burr told a friend, "I suppose I should be grateful to heaven for providing one at this particular moment. But the main thing is that I want to go to work again. If you'd care to do me one service, I'd be very grateful. You see, my funds right now are a trifle limited. Limited, in fact, to exactly twelve cents. If you could advance me a little capital, say, ten dollars . . . ?"

"Oh, but surely, sir, you must take more than that," his friend, Robert Troup said. "It's only fair, considering that I owe you everything I have. If you hadn't helped me through my law work, and bought me all my books, as well as food and clothes and——"

"Please, Robert"—Mr. Burr shook his head, laughing—"spare me a catalogue of my good deeds. They're forgotten, I hope, as completely as my bad ones. Ten dollars will be quite enough, I promise you. I shall rent an office immediately. And then," he finished with a shrug, "we shall see if I have any clients left."

That same afternoon a single room in a modest building at Number 23, Nassau Street, was engaged by a slight, unassuming gentleman in a shabby blue coat.

"A queer sort of chap, he seems," the landlady confided later to her husband. "Quiet-like, not too young, but lively as a cricket, he was, sweeping out the place himself and wheedling an old table and chair for furnishings."

She went to the window and looked down curiously. The "lively little chap" was just then engaged in tacking a small painted sign outside the door. He had scarcely driven the last tack before his first client came knocking. And there was a steady stream to follow.

With the advent of war, there was a bumper crop of law business in New York that year, and plenty of people recalled that Aaron Burr had once had the reputation of never losing a case.

If anyone bothered to recall that Mr. Burr had once been in prison, they only shrugged and echoed the words of his landlady. "Let bygones be bygones."

Soon the small room at 23 Nassau Street was crowded with clients. The rickety table and chair were replaced by newer furniture. There were lawbooks on the shelves now and, in one corner, a leather couch on which Mr. Burr slept.

If, his landlady observed, he slept at all, which she doubted, as she never looked in at the door but what she found him still bent over his books in the candlelight.

Once, being up late herself because of a toothache, she stopped in to offer Mr. Burr a hot cup of tea. He seemed very pleased, pushing his spectacles up on his forehead and leaning back in his chair to chat as politely as you please while he drank. She noticed over the fireplace a picture of a pretty young lady, very elegant and fine, with dark curly hair and a handsome white dress. When she asked Mr. Burr who the lady was, a queer look came into his dark eyes, that usually looked sharp as gimlets, for all their merry twinkling.

"That is my daughter, madam," he said after a minute.

She was surprised to think such a plain little man would have a daughter who looked like a great lady.

To Theodosia nothing could have been sweeter news than the reports of her father's reception and occupation in New York.

"You remember," she said to Joseph one evening, "Papa used to say then that if fortune's wheel turned down, it was only a question of time before it would turn up again. And he was right, for it really has, at last."

"I had a letter from him today," Joseph said, "full of all sorts of advice about running for governor."

They were out on the piazza, watching the last rays of the June twilight fade gently over the gardens. Even with the sun gone, there was little relief from the sweltering heat and the faint breeze from the south brought only the heaviness of swamp vapors.

"I do wish the wind would change." Theodosia sighed. "Dr. Logan says there's always more fever when the swamp winds blow, and it makes the mosquitoes worse than ever." She brushed at one that buzzed persistently about her head. "Do you think there's any chance of our getting away to the island fairly soon, Joseph?"

"You and Aaron can go at once if you like. In fact, I'd feel easier if you would. But I'll have to stay until we have some definite news from Washington about the war, and heaven only knows when that will come."

Presently young Aaron wandered up the path from the paddock and sat down on the piazza steps. His dark hair clung damply about his flushed cheeks, and there was a beading of moisture on his upper lip.

"Aaron, dear"—Theodosia leaned forward anxiously—"you look dreadfully hot. Surely you haven't been riding on an evening like this?"

"Oh, just a few turns around the paddock." As his mother reached out to touch his forehead, he drew away impatiently. "I'm all *right,* Mum." He turned to Joseph. "Is it true we're going to declare war most any day now, Father?"

"I'm afraid so, Aaron."

"Pete says he's going to be a sailor, if we do. I wish I could go with him. Pete says they're building a new schooner in Charleston, and that's the one he wants to be on. It's going to be named the *Saucy Jack,* and it'll have sixteen guns, Pete says. Is that *true,* Father?"

Joseph nodded. "You can't go to war just yet, Aaron," he said, "but, if you like, I'll arrange for you to be taken aboard the day they launch the *Jack.*"

"*Honestly,* father?" The boy jumped up, his dark eyes shining with eager excitement. "And, Father, do you think if I asked, very specially, they might let me wear one of those caps the sailors have? You know, with letters on the ribbon?"

"I shouldn't be surprised," Joseph said, "if you were to ask *very* specially."

## CHAPTER 23

# Success to the Saucy Jack

THE NEXT MORNING the long-awaited word came from Washington.

All day the harbor thundered with the salute of booming guns, and at noon the South Battery was thronged with people who gathered round to hear the sheriff read President Madison's formal proclamation of war.

From all over Charleston young men hurried to enlist, and the highways leading into town swarmed with carts and wagons, bringing planters eager to volunteer against the enemy that had for so long plundered their cargoes of rice and corn and indigo, and throttled the commerce of the once thriving port. One young fellow shook his fist toward the harbor where, just out of sight, the British vessels lay in wait.

"Just let 'em wait," he cried, above the cheers of the crowd and the sound of rolling drums. "They'll jolly well find out that England doesn't own *our* ocean!"

It was after dusk when Joseph got home that evening.

The candles burned quietly in their tall brackets on either side of the wide hall, but oddly there was no sign of Theodosia.

Joseph went upstairs, his footsteps echoing in the silence of the house. Then, as he paused on the upper landing, the door of Aaron's bedroom opened, and Theodosia came out to meet him.

"Joseph"—she spoke quietly, but her eyes were dark and tragic—"oh, Joseph!" She slipped into his arms with a quivering breath. "I'm so glad you've come. Aaron's ill and I'm so frightened."

It was the fever again.

Shortly after breakfast Aaron had been taken with a chill. Dr. Logan had been sent for. He was with Aaron now, sitting beside the bed in the darkened room where the boy lay.

"He says there's nothing more we can do now, Joseph, except to wait," Theodosia whispered. "But I was afraid—terribly afraid—until you came."

For four days and nights all life in the big house seemed suspended. The servants spoke in hushed voices, tiptoeing about through the silent rooms. Then, a little after twilight on the last day of June, the boy's thin body gave up its gallant fight to live. Dr. Logan, his young face drawn and weary, looked across the bed to Theodosia and Joseph.

"I'm sorry," he said, in a queer, gruff voice. "I—did the best I could."

Late that evening a man knocked at the broad front door of the Oaks. He had a message for Mr. Alston. Very urgent.

The servant tried to turn him away, but there was a step in the hall, and Joseph came to the door.

"What is it you want?"

"I have a message, Mr. Alston. You've just been appointed commander of the militia for the state of South Carolina. You're wanted at headquarters, sir, just as soon as possible . . ." The man hesitated, sensing something strange in the silence. "I—I'm sorry to've disturbed you, sir, only they said I mustn't fail to tell you tonight. And they say, sir"— he paused again, turning his hat uncertainly—"that this means you're sure to be elected governor."

Joseph still said nothing for a moment. Then he lifted his shoulders. "If you'll be good enough to wait," he said, "I'll have a horse saddled and ride back to town with you. Only first"—he turned slowly back toward the stairs—"I must tell my wife."

It was a winter's day, mild and bright, when Joseph took the oath of office as Governor of South Carolina. Riding beside him in the open carriage drawn by four white horses, Theodosia looked out at the people who lined the flag-draped streets leading to the Capitol steps. Many of them had known Joseph during his years in the legislature, and as the carriage passed they called out greetings. Joseph, his dark head bare in the winter sunlight, bowed to this side and that.

As they moved slowly along, Theodosia sat very still. Her hand rested quietly on her husband's arm, while she smiled at the lines of cheering people. Only once, when the carriage halted briefly at a crowded corner, she leaned forward suddenly, to look at a boy who stood on the edge of the curb waving a small silk flag. He was a merry-looking lad, about ten years old, but there was nothing about his freckled face to attract particular attention. Nothing—except that he wore a sailor's cap, jauntily tipped on his head, and written in bright gold letters on the ribbon band were the words "Success to the *Saucy Jack.*"

For just a moment then, the smile faltered on Theodosia's lips. The memory of her lost son stabbed her like a knife.

The carriage moved forward, and she turned quickly to Joseph. There was nothing in his expression to show that he had seen, but for an instant his hand closed over hers. She felt the gentle pressure of his fingers.

"All right, Theo?"

"All right, Joseph," she whispered back. And her smile, as she looked up into his blue eyes, was steady once more.

A few days after the inauguration the Alstons returned to Charleston. Ever since Mr. Burr's return to New York, it had been planned that they were to go north for a visit with him as soon as the trip could be arranged. But with Joseph's doubly important duties as governor and commander of the state militia, there was no telling when he might be able to go.

Why not then, Mr. Burr had written, have Theodosia come alone?

Joseph was doubtful. He agreed with Mr. Burr that the visit and a change of climate would be the best possible tonic for his wife. But the trip by land was long and fatiguing, and not considered safe for a woman alone. And sea travel, with the country at war, was none too certain either. Finally it was suggested that Dr. Timothy Greene, an old friend of Mr. Burr, would go to Charleston and accompany Theodosia, and to this plan Joseph gave his consent.

Dr. Greene arrived, preparations for the journey were made, and on the last day of December, Theodosia and Lottie, escorted by the kindly, gray-haired physician, boarded the schooner *Patriot*.

Theodosia's spirits had revived amazingly with the prospect of the trip. At the dock, where Joseph and Natalie had come to see her off, she bade them good-by cheerfully and, for the first time in many months, there was color in her cheeks and a sparkle of eagerness in her dark eyes.

Natalie had brought a parcel of new books and a woolen muffler for Mr. Burr.

"You won't forget to tell Papa I knitted the muffler myself," she said anxiously, "so he'll excuse the lumps in it. And be sure to give him my dearest love, Theo—and John and Frederic, too."

"Of course I will." Theodosia kissed her cheek. "You must keep an eye on Joseph for me. See that he doesn't work too hard, and don't let his head be turned altogether by too many ladies casting sheep's eyes at the handsome new governor."

"Don't worry. I shall guard him like a dragon," Natalie promised.

Theodosia turned to her husband for one last moment.

"I do wish you were going too, Joseph," she said, her voice suddenly forlorn. "But I shall come home soon, you know—quite soon."

## ·CHAPTER 24·

# New Year's Eve

IT WAS A little after ten o'clock that night when the storm broke.

All up and down the Carolina coast the sea raged, driven by the fury of the wind. Great waves, rolling inward over the long sand bars outside Currituck and Pamlico sounds, dashed themselves against the lonely beaches with a thunder that mingled with the high drone of the wind.

It was New Year's Eve.

In the houses of Charleston people were celebrating. Safe from the storm that shuddered and thundered outside, they raised their glasses to toast health and good fortune as the stroke of midnight was tolled. The bells of old St. Michael's rang loudest, their bronze voices pitched deep and clear against the sound of thunder.

"Victory," the toast was given. "Victory to the United States."

Somewhere off the Carolina coast, making its way through the black sea, was a small schooner pilot boat. In the lighted dining saloon the passengers huddled together, seeking comfort from the storm in each other's presence. There, too, glasses were raised at the stroke of midnight and a toast was given.

"To the New Year—and a safe journey."

North of the Carolinas, along the sand bars that lay off the treacherous coast, there were settlements of a strange, half-wild people called *"bankers."* Descendants of the fierce and bold pirates who had for years roamed the coastal waters, these ragged, long-haired derelicts no longer sailed the seas, but were content to wait, like vultures, for ships that might founder along the shoal waters on such a night as this, delivering their victims of the storm into the bankers' plundering and murderous hands.

Under cover of the black, wild night, the bankers lay in wait for disaster. Along the sand bars of Kitty Hawk and Nags Head, they led an old horse up and down the shore, a lantern tied about its neck, so the bobbing, wavering beam of light might lure passing ships to a false haven from the angry sea. Up and down, up and down, through the driving fury of the night, the old nag stumbled along the uneven shore.

Only one passenger was missing from the little company in the schooner's dining room. A young woman, dressed in gray, who had come aboard just before they sailed. She had slipped away quietly, a little after dinner, and no one appeared to notice her absence. But shortly after midnight an elderly gentleman left the group and made his way to the second deck where he tapped at a cabin door.

"Come in."

Dr. Greene entered.

Theodosia was sitting alone in the small, lighted cabin, her hands folded in her lap. "I expect you've come to tell me I ought to go to bed, Doctor," she said, "and so I shall—presently. I didn't mean to alarm you by coming off alone. I'm quite all right, truly."

The doctor steadied himself as the ship gave a sudden heave, her timbers groaning before the angry buffeting of the sea.

"I thought perhaps the storm had frightened you."

She shook her head. "Not very much. Poor Lottie was wretched with a headache. I sent her to bed an hour ago. I've been thinking . . ." She paused, looking up. "You know, Doctor, it seems as if I'd never had so many things to think about. A great deal has happened to me lately. So much, really, that I hadn't stopped to realize it all until tonight. Some things have been good, and some . . ." She paused again, and let the words trail away. "But it will be wonderful to see my father. It's been a long while, you know, and we shall have so much to say. That's what I was thinking of mostly."

"I'll leave you to your thoughts then." The doctor turned away, but at the door he looked back. "Only mind, you mustn't sit up too late."

"I won't. I promise."

"Good night, then." He closed the cabin door on his last sight of her. She was looking up at him, the lamplight shining softly on the dark waves of her hair and catching a gleam of gold from a locket that hung at the throat of her plain gray gown. Sitting there, serene and smiling, she might have been in her own bedroom at home, instead of in a cramped, close cabin, on a small boat, in the twisting fury of a black and storm-swept sea.

A full week passed after the dawn of the New Year, but still the schooner *Patriot* had not reached New York. The boat must have been delayed—thrown off her course, perhaps, by the storm. Or she might have been overtaken by a British boat and forced to land her passengers at some port along the way. Surely, in a few days more, there would be news. . . .

Another week passed, and then another—and still no word.

Frantic messages passed from Mr. Burr in New York to Joseph in Charleston. "Have you had no news?" . . . "No, none." Nothing was known, nothing had been heard since the December afternoon when the *Patriot* sailed out of Charleston harbor.

Rumors began to come then. Rumors of a wreck, of a crew that had mutinied, and plundered and burned the ship, forcing the passengers to walk the plank. Rumors that the ship had foundered off the Carolina coast and fallen into the evil hands of the bankers. Rumors that the ship had been sunk by the British because she was carrying a cargo of contraband.

But they were only rumors. Gradually, as time passed, they died away into the mist of doubt from which they had come. With their death the last lingering hope died, too. There was nothing to wait for now. No answer to heartbroken questions came from the silent, restless sea which alone knew the end of the lost schooner *Patriot* and all her passengers and crew.

Theodosia was gone. None of those who loved her and waited for her ever knew her fate.

Sometimes, on a winter's afternoon, the gentleman at Number 23, Nassau Street, would leave his busy office for an hour and walk down to Battery Park. There, among the fashionable ladies and gentlemen who strolled along, arm in arm, he would be seen standing alone by the embankment rail, looking down the Narrows to the sea. He would seem, for a time, to be watching for someone, with a curious, expectant look in his dark eyes.

After a while, the gentleman would turn and walk quickly away. . . .

*Anne Colver* was thirteen when she first heard of Theodosia Burr, and decided someday to write her biography. The author has had eighteen books published, but *Theodosia* remains a favorite of hers because the idea was her first for a book.

She attended Friends school in Washington, D.C. and Pine Manor Junior College, then graduated from Whitman College in Washington state. After writing five mysteries, she turned to historical fiction. The Early American period, the era of the Burr family, is one of her specialities.

Anne Colver lives in Irvington-on-Hudson, New York, with her husband, a lawyer and writer, and their daughter, Kate.